Contents

The problem

In recent years the building industry has undergone substantial change. Buildings must now meet more exacting and varied performance requirements. Mechanical, electrical and other services now comprise a major portion of a typical building. There is a much greater range of materials and methods of construction. The industry has become more industrialised and mechanised, and buildings are constructed more quickly.

There has also been substantial organisational change. Specialist design consultants are now used more frequently, so that the information for projects is invariably produced by several different people. Most construction work is now subcontracted so that even within the 'traditional' building contract the 'general contractor' has become not so much a builder as a manager of work carried out by others.

Because of the greater number of people involved in both producing and using project information, there is an increased risk of misunderstanding and oversight; the quality and co-ordination of the project information has therefore become more important. Unfortunately the changes in the industry have not, so far, had a corresponding impact on the documents which the industry uses for its organisation and management.

The availability, reliability and ease of assimilation of project information are known to be critical to the effective pricing, planning, execution and control of building work. Despite this the content, structuring and timing of drawings is highly variable from office to office and job to job. The quality of project specifications is also variable but generally low, good information cannot be distinguished from bad, so the specification is rarely used in the management and control of the work. Bills of quantities are required to comply with SMM, which has changed little over the years; in consequence doubts have developed as to whether bills are sufficiently simple to meet present day needs and sufficiently representative of the pattern of sub-contracting. The drawings, specifications and quantities are prepared by design teams which often vary from job to job: the relative absence of common procedures and a common information structure thus all too easily leads to poor co-ordination.

Deficiencies in project information can be classified as follows:

- Missing – information not produced, or not distributed to site.
- Late – not available in time to plan the work or order the materials.
- Incorrect – errors of description, reference or dimension; out of date information.
- Insufficient detail – e.g. even if adequate for pricing, not so for construction.
- Impractical – difficult to construct.
- Inappropriate – information not entirely relevant or suitable for its purpose.
- Unclear – e.g. because of poor drafting or ambiguity.
- Not firm – provisional information often indistinguishable from firm information.
- Poorly arranged – poor and inconsistent structure, unclear titling.
- Unco-ordinated – difficult to read one document with another.
- Conflicting – documents which disagree with each other.

It is believed that deficiencies in project information contribute significantly to major problems within the industry including:

- The incidence of technical defects in finished buildings.
- The frequently poor quality of finished work, related to high maintenance costs.
- The frequency of variations and consequential uncertainty as to the final cost.
- The high level of claims being made by contractors.
- The late completion of many contracts.

These matters cannot be regarded as characteristics of an efficient industry. They indicate that an excessive proportion of skilled time is devoted to sorting out problems retrospectively rather than avoiding them in the first place.

The problem as seen on site

Between 1978 and 1983 the Building Research Establishment carried out a study of 38 building sites to determine the causes of variations in the level of quality being achieved.* The projects were reasonably typical, including a variety of sizes and building types, public and private sector projects and both traditional and novel forms of contract. A BRE researcher was stationed full time on each site for 2–3 weeks, having full access to the works and all documents, and in close contact with the supervisory personnel.

Causes of quality problems

The BRE observers assessed the general levels of quality being produced, and made particular note of 'quality problems' and why they occurred. By far the two most frequent causes were lack of care by tradesmen and unclear/missing project information. Many of the problems were of a trivial nature, but a worrying proportion were serious, involving such things as water ingress, long term stability and unacceptable appearance. On average, site staff were identifying 2½ serious problems per week, and despite the efforts of all concerned to remedy them, one serious problem per week remained with either an unsatisfactory solution or no solution at all. The majority of serious problems were caused by either poor design, inadequate project information, or poor organisation by the building contractor.

Effect of information on quality

Most of the sites which exhibited good quality had been provided with reasonably complete and timely project information. In many cases the designers had put much effort into planning and preparing the production drawings and/or a comprehensive NBS type specification. Contractors for the better quality projects tended to make themselves acquainted with the programme of drawings production and contributed to the resolution of hold-ups or gaps in the information flow.

Figure A shows the relationship between quality of information and quality of work for all 38 sites. In some cases the quality of information was patchy (e.g. good for the building fabric but poor for the services, or a full specification but incomplete

General quality of information: completeness and promptness of drawings and specification and quality of information support provided on site	**Quality of finished work**			
	Poor	Average	Good	
Very poor	2	–	–	2
Poor	4	9	3	16
Medium	1	–	9	10
Good	1	–	3	4
Excellent	–	–	6	6
	8	9	21	

Figure A Survey of 38 projects : effect of project information on quality of work (for more detail see Appendices 1, 2 and 3)

* BRE Current Paper 7/81 'Quality control on building sites'

'Achievement of quality on building sites' NEDO 1987

drawings). In other cases the designers compensated for poor drawings and specification by spending a lot of time on site filling in gaps in the information as they arose. But virtually half the sites had generally poor or very poor information, and had a high incidence of poor quality work.

Late and inadequate information

The study indicated that late arrival of drawings is a fact of life for most site managers. Not surprisingly, late drawings are often hastily produced – just the type of drawings site agents and clerks of works need to check well in advance of construction to discover any discrepancies or ambiguities.

Contractors' staff spent much time trying to fill gaps in information rather than seek clarification. One reason for this was that requests for clarification were often dealt with relatively slowly by the design team, even on design and build projects where the contractor has control over the design process. The time taken in chasing and filling in for overdue information was inevitably 'stolen' from the time that site agents and clerks of works would otherwise have had for supervising the execution of the work.

Site management

Figure B shows the effect of contractors' management on quality. A key factor was the contractor's choice of sub-contractors. The competence and diligence of the site agent and trades foremen in controlling the work, identifying information problems and contributing to their solution had a strong influence on the quality of the work.

Clerks of works, where appointed, had a variable influence on quality. Much of their time was spent in helping to sort out information problems and their effectiveness in doing this was largely dependent on their ability to elicit information from the designers. Clerks of works usually had to make a choice as to how to spend their time most effectively – responding to the contractor's requests for information or monitoring the quality of the work. Their effectiveness in this latter function depended in large measure on the backing which they received from the architect and/or client.

Figure B
Survey of 38 projects : effect of contractors' management on quality of work (for more detail see Appendices 1, 2 and 3)

Quality of management	Quality of finished work			
	Poor	Average	Good	
Poor	6	1	2	9
Medium	2	5	2	9
Good	–	3	17	20
	8	9	21	

Implications for designers

It will be seen from Figure A that excellent project information is highly likely to result in good quality work, and very poor project information is highly likely to result in poor quality work. Where the project information is of an average standard it is usually possible for a good site agent, assisted by a good clerk of works, to overcome most of the problems to achieve an acceptable standard of quality. Unfortunately, at pre-tender stage, when the quality, comprehensiveness and timeliness of the project information is largely determined, the quality of the contractor's site management is usually not known. The BRE study included several cases where careful selection of the tendering contractor(s) did not result in good site management.

Thus when the information is of an indifferent or average standard, the chances of getting good quality of work are probably not much better than 50–50. The implication is that the most effective way of influencing quality open to the designer is to produce complete and timely project information.

The BRE study was concerned with quality of work; the effects of project information on contractual cost and progress were not measured. However many of the quality problems identified by the BRE observers will inevitably increase the cost of future maintenance. Also, earlier BRE research into one aspect of documentation* had shown that over 700 conflicts between drawings occurred on a sample of 25 building projects, and that most of these caused abortive or additional work – see Figure C.

Although not covered by BRE research, it is widely recognised that incomplete and late project information often affects progress and leads to extensions of time. Project information which is incomplete at tender stage often brings in its train a high incidence of variations and a final cost higher than the client expected. Once again, the implication is that designers should, whenever they can, produce complete and timely project information.

* BRE Current Paper 60/76 'Co-ordinating working drawings'

Figure C
Types of conflict between drawings and their effect on site working (From BRE Current Paper 60/76 'Co-ordinating working drawings').

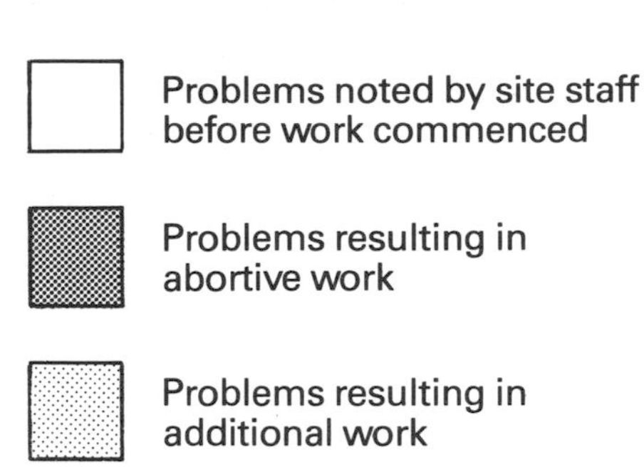

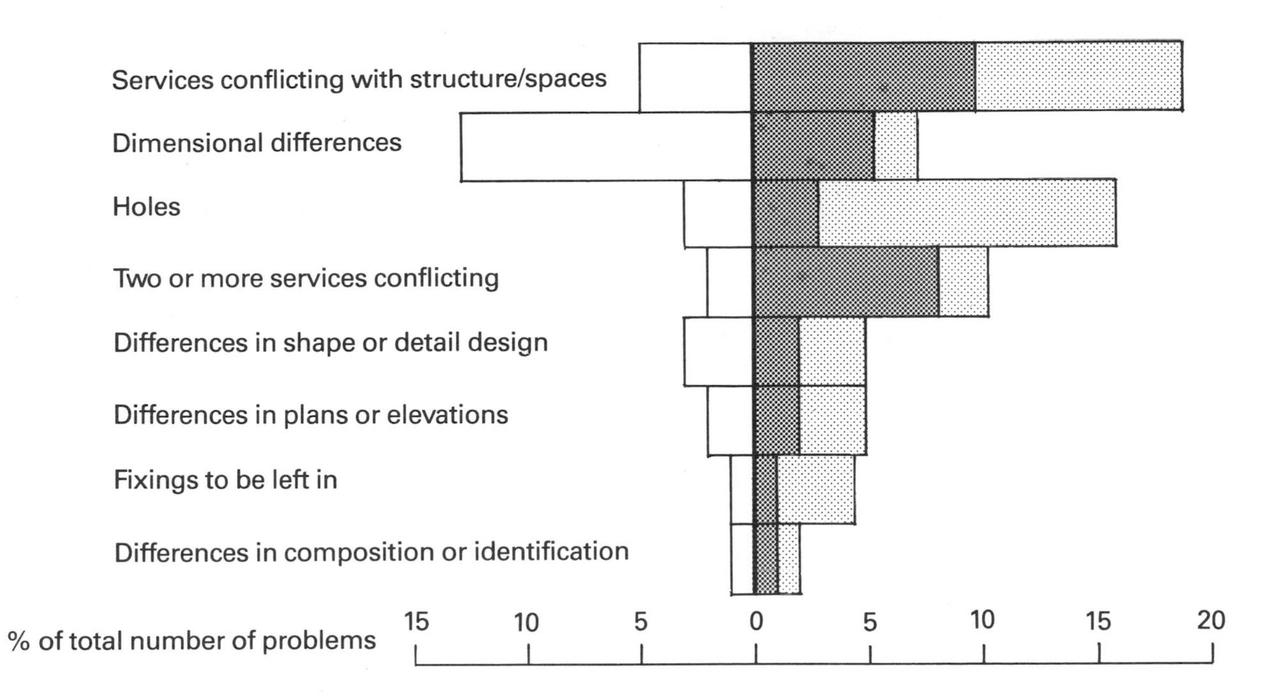

The problem as seen in the design office

During 1980–1 the York Institute of Advanced Architectural Studies made a study of 12 live design projects in a variety of types and sizes of architects' offices.* The main aim was to investigate the use of information in the design process, but as background to this the general pattern of work in the offices was also studied.

Inherent complexity of design

The study showed that the design process is complex and unpredictable, far more so than is generally understood by non-designers. Seemingly minor aspects of design are often critical to the feasibility of a more general proposal, and thus need to be resolved at an early stage. Conversely, quite major decisions can often be made quickly on the basis of previous experience, permitting postponement of work until a later stage in the confident knowledge that the details should work. The stages of design for different elements of a building are therefore, in practice, progressed at different rates so that it is seldom possible to define in simple terms the degree of completion which a project has reached at any particular time.

*IAAS Research Paper 19, 'Design decision making in architectural practice' 1982.

Uncontrollable delays

The study showed that design projects are vulnerable to disruption, delay, postponement or abandonment. The most significant problems observed during the study were:

- Information from clients, e.g. incomplete briefing, lack of clarity as to requirements, changes in requirements during the progress of the design.
- Site acquisition.
- Cost trimming, either because the client decided to reduce the budget or because the architect's ideas exceeded it.
- Statutory approvals, particularly planning approval.

Because of these external influences, designs progress intermittently and at irregular speeds. Designers find it difficult to plan their workloads well in advance and invariably have only short notice of a new commission or the removal of a hold-up to an existing commission. They need to have a certain volume of work in hand all the time, to allow for unexpected delays on individual projects. Most of the designers included in the York study, particularly those in the smaller offices, were therefore having to look after several projects at a time, some at different stages of the design process and some on site. That the average designer is concerned with such a range of work at any one time is generally not well recognised by non-designers, including clients.

Excessive fragmentation of work

The picture revealed by the study is therefore of an inherently complex and unpredictable process being further complicated by having to work on different stages of different projects at the same time. If a designer is involved in jobs at tender stage or on site he will have to deal with queries from manufacturers, builders or clerks of works at any time of day and not pre-arranged to fit in with breaks in other work. This inevitably causes disruption, particularly as certain stages of the design process require periods of concentrated attention.

It was observed that the architect's typical day is extremely fragmented. His plan for what he will do each day is normally frustrated – in practice he has to deal with several quite different problems arising out of the blue. The only exception to this is in larger, more specialised offices where designers do not have to work on so many projects at one time.

Shortage of time

The study concluded that the variety of tasks and jobs with which the average designer is occupied over even short periods of time appears to have considerable effects on productivity. In a number of respects architects were shown to be left with insufficient time for their work:

- Only a small proportion of the available relevant written information was consulted, reliance being placed on memory and experience.
- Design decisions were poorly recorded, so that it was often difficult to backtrack or pick up the threads when a job had been delayed.
- Drawings and other documents prepared by junior staff were not checked rigorously.

Implications for designers

The York study was concerned solely with architectural practice, but many of its conclusions are likely to apply to other design professions. The findings of the study seem consistent with the BRE studies of work on site: the frequent lateness and poor co-ordination of information and the difficulties of getting prompt answers to site queries are made more understandable.

Most design office activity is pre-contract, when the client is rarely under an obligation to proceed and there is a high probability of delays and changes so that planning and ordered progress are often impossible. However once projects are on site the various parties have a joint contractual obligation to proceed according to a predetermined programme. Overlaps between design and construction therefore involve the juxtaposition of two fundamentally different management systems. The result is that information required by site staff is often not provided expeditiously, and other design work is constantly interrupted. Where such overlaps occur it is clearly desirable that the post-contract production of information is firmly programmed and adequately resourced.

It would be unrealistic to postulate the completion of all drawings and specification pre-tender, but it is clear that practice should move closer to that ideal. The York study gives some useful pointers to how this might be achieved without increasing design costs:

- A considerable amount of abortive work in architects' offices is because of incomplete briefing, and the client changing his mind during the design process. Architects could be more diligent in seeking proper briefing information and helping their clients to be more decisive.
- Delays due to finance, budgets, site acquisition and statutory approvals mean that designers have to work on several jobs simultaneously, and cannot plan their work effectively. More effective anticipation of such problems is needed.
- The extreme fragmentation of the designer's daily activities adversely affects his productivity. If drawings and specification were, as a matter of general practice, to be substantially complete at tender stage, the incidence of queries during tender action and construction would be substantially reduced – the gains in productivity would, in turn, make it easier to complete the contract documents on time in the first place.

How CPI will help

The problem of unco-ordinated project information has arisen because the professions have developed their own conventions and working habits independently. The various members of the industry are not independent; if they are to be fully effective they must act in a more collaborative and co-ordinated manner. The conventions produced by multi disciplinary effort under the auspices of CCPI (see inside front cover) provide a clear basis for such action.

The conventions seek to promote co-ordination by giving recommendations of three main types:

- Procedures for producing documents, e.g. planning the set of drawings to minimise duplication and maximise use of copy negatives, techniques for co-ordinating services drawings, use of libraries of clauses as a systematic way of recording specification decisions.
- Technical content of documents, e.g. annotation of drawings, detailed checklists for the content of project specifications, revised rules for measurement.
- Arrangement of documents, e.g. structuring of drawn information by type, use of the Common arrangement for both specifications and quantities.

Co-ordinated project information has important implications for contractors. More complete, timely, relevant and conveniently arranged information should enable them to estimate, plan and control building work more efficiently to produce buildings of good quality, on time and within cost.

At present, the building process can be risky for clients because of uncertainties about the performance of the many individuals involved and their ability to work together effectively. Co-ordinated project information should significantly reduce the client's risk regardless of type and size of project and regardless of contractual arrangement. Clients may therefore wish to consider specifying compliance with the co-ordinated conventions when negotiating fees with their professional advisers.

The co-ordinated conventions

Common arrangement of work sections

The purpose of the 'Common arrangement of work sections' (CAWS) is to define an efficient and generally acceptable identical arrangement for specifications and bills of quantities. The main advantages which should accrue are:

Easier distribution of information

Traditional specifications and quantities are arranged in about 15–20 'trade' sections. The division of information for sub-contracting is usually much finer than this so that the contractor has unnecessary work in dividing up and editing the information. A set of common categories at this finer level should make it easier to divide information for distribution to sub-contractors and suppliers both for estimating and subsequently for construction.

More effective reading together of documents

A traditional bill of quantities with trade preambles is co-ordinated in the sense that the whole specification text for each trade corresponds with all the bill items for each trade. However, many trades are so large that it is often difficult to relate a bill item to a particular group of specification statements and vice versa. An arrangement which divides work into much smaller sections should facilitate such reading together and encourage designers, when annotating their drawings, to incorporate simple but precise references to the relevant clauses of the specification.

Greater consistency of content and description

Traditional documents are variable both in technical content and the way in which they describe things. Sometimes the measured item descriptions are long, sometimes brief. Sometimes the specification is bulky, sometimes brief. Wider use of standard specification clauses would give greater consistency of content and description. A common arrangement supported by detailed section definitions should make the relationship between specifications and quantities more reliable, promoting a more consistent level of description in the quantities. Additionally, the use of cross-references to the specification should encourage designers to be more consistent in the amount of description which they give on drawings. The overall effect should be to make the amount of information in the individual project documents less variable, and to give greater predictability as to the location of information. There should be less repetition and the documents should be simpler to use.

The work sections

CAWS includes about 300 work sections. They are derived from close observation of the current pattern of sub-contracting in the industry. They vary widely in their scope and nature, reflecting the large range of building materials, products, specialists and sub-contractors which now exist. The new arrangement has been the subject of wide consultation within the industry.

The primary factors which influence and define the work sections are:

- Responsibility for design and performance.
- Methods of working, related to sub-contract practice.

Definitions are provided for all sections – three examples are given on page 13.

Arrangement and coding

CAWS is set out in three levels, the third and lowest of these being the work sections. Levels 1 and 2 are not work sections so much as headings under which the work sections are grouped. To reinforce this distinction the three levels have been given the following titles:

Level 1: Group	(e.g. D	Groundwork)
Level 2: Sub-group	(e.g. D3	Piling)
Level 3: Work section	(e.g. D30	Cast in place concrete piling)

The three levels provide a classified grouping which will permit new sections to be inserted in the future. Project specifications and bills of quantities will be most clearly and simply arranged using only Level 1 and Level 3 headings.

The full list of Level 1 and Level 3 headings is given on pages 9 to 12. The comprehensive coverage and 'narrow scope' approach have resulted in a tenfold increase in the number of work sections compared with traditional practice. However it will be found that only 10–30% of the sections will apply to any one project.

Implementation

The co-ordinated conventions listed on the inside of the front cover (with the sole exception of the Code for production drawings) are all being arranged by CAWS. The PSA General Specification will be changed to CAWS format during 1988. BSI and the CI/SfB Agency are considering the possible future use of CAWS in the structuring of Standards and the classification of technical literature.

The work sections and their grouping

A Preliminaries/General conditions

A10 Project particulars
A11 Drawings
A12 The site/Existing buildings
A13 Description of the work

A20 The Contract/Sub-contract

A30 Employer's requirements: Tendering/Sub-letting/Supply
A31 Employer's requirements: Provision, content and use of documents
A32 Employer's requirements: Management of the Works
A33 Employer's requirements: Quality standards/control
A34 Employer's requirements: Security/Safety/Protection
A35 Employer's requirements: Specific limitations on method/sequence/timing
A36 Employer's requirements: Facilities/Temporary works/Services
A37 Employer's requirements: Operation/Maintenance of the finished building

A40 Contractor's costs: Management and staff
A41 Contractor's costs: Site accommodation
A42 Contractor's costs: Services and facilities
A43 Contractor's costs: Mechanical plant
A44 Contractor's costs: Temporary works

A50 Work/Materials by the Employer
A51 Nominated sub-contractors
A52 Nominated suppliers
A53 Work by statutory authorities
A54 Provisional work
A55 Dayworks

B Complete buildings

B10 Proprietary buildings

C Demolition/Alteration/Renovation

C10 Demolishing structures

C20 Alterations – spot items

C30 Shoring

C40 Repairing/Renovating concrete/brick/block/stone
C41 Chemical dpcs to existing walls

C50 Repairing/Renovating metal
C51 Repairing/Renovating timber
C52 Fungus/Beetle eradication

D Groundwork

D10 Ground investigation
D11 Soil stabilization
D12 Site dewatering

D20 Excavating and filling

D30 Cast in place concrete piling
D31 Preformed concrete piling
D32 Steel piling

D40 Diaphragm walling

D50 Underpinning

E In situ concrete/Large precast concrete

E10 In situ concrete
E11 Gun applied concrete

E20 Formwork for in situ concrete

E30 Reinforcement for in situ concrete
E31 Post tensioned reinforcement for in situ concrete

E40 Designed joints in in situ concrete
E41 Worked finishes/Cutting to in situ concrete
E42 Accessories cast into in situ concrete

E50 Precast concrete large units

E60 Precast/Composite concrete decking

F Masonry

F10 Brick/Block walling
F11 Glass block walling

F20 Natural stone rubble walling
F21 Natural stone/ashlar walling/dressings
F22 Cast stone walling/dressings

F30 Accessories/Sundry items for brick/block/stone walling
F31 Precast concrete sills/lintels/copings/features

G Structural/Carcassing metal/timber

G10 Structural steel framing
G11 Structural aluminium framing
G12 Isolated structural metal members

G20 Carpentry/Timber framing/First fixing

G30 Metal profiled sheet decking
G31 Prefabricated timber unit decking
G32 Edge supported/Reinforced woodwool slab decking

H Cladding/Covering

H10 Patent glazing
H11 Curtain walling
H12 Plastics glazed vaulting/walling
H13 Structural glass assemblies
H14 Concrete rooflights/pavement lights

H20 Rigid sheet cladding
H21 Timber weatherboarding

H30 Fibre cement profiled sheet cladding/covering/siding
H31 Metal profiled/flat sheet cladding/covering/siding
H32 Plastics profiled sheet cladding/covering/siding
H33 Bitumen and fibre profiled sheet cladding/covering

H40 Glass reinforced cement cladding/features
H41 Glass reinforced plastics cladding/features

H50 Precast concrete slab cladding/features
H51 Natural stone slab cladding/features
H52 Cast stone slab cladding/features

H60 Clay/Concrete roof tiling
H61 Fibre cement slating
H62 Natural slating
H63 Reconstructed stone slating/tiling
H64 Timber shingling

H70 Malleable metal sheet prebonded coverings/cladding
H71 Lead sheet coverings/flashings
H72 Aluminium sheet coverings/flashings
H73 Copper sheet coverings/flashings
H74 Zinc sheet coverings/flashings
H75 Stainless steel sheet coverings/flashings
H76 Fibre bitumen thermoplastic sheet coverings/flashings

J Waterproofing

J10 Specialist waterproof rendering

J20 Mastic asphalt tanking/damp proof membranes
J21 Mastic asphalt roofing/insulation/finishes
J22 Proprietary roof decking with asphalt finish

J30 Liquid applied tanking/damp proof membranes
J31 Liquid applied waterproof roof coatings
J32 Sprayed vapour barriers
J33 In situ glass reinforced plastics

J40 Flexible sheet tanking/damp proof membranes
J41 Built up felt roof coverings
J42 Single layer plastics roof coverings
J43 Proprietary roof decking with felt finish

K Linings/Sheathing/Dry partitioning

K10 Plasterboard dry lining
K11 Rigid sheet flooring/sheathing/linings/casings
K12 Under purlin/Inside rail panel linings
K13 Rigid sheet fine linings/panelling

K20 Timber board flooring/sheathing/linings/casings
K21 Timber narrow strip flooring/linings

K30 Demountable partitions
K31 Plasterboard fixed partitions/inner walls/linings
K32 Framed panel cubicle partitions
K33 Concrete/Terrazzo partitions

K40 Suspended ceilings
K41 Raised access floors

L Windows/Doors/Stairs

L10 Timber windows/rooflights/screens/louvres
L11 Metal windows/rooflights/screens/louvres
L12 Plastics windows/rooflights/screens/louvres

L20 Timber doors/shutters/hatches
L21 Metal doors/shutters/hatches
L22 Plastics/Rubber doors/shutters/hatches

L30 Timber stairs/walkways/balustrades
L31 Metal stairs/walkways/balustrades

L40 General glazing
L41 Lead light glazing
L42 Infill panels/sheets

M Surface finishes

M10 Sand cement/Concrete/Granolithic screeds/flooring
M11 Mastic asphalt flooring
M12 Trowelled bitumen/resin/rubber-latex flooring

M20 Plastered/Rendered/Roughcast coatings
M21 Insulation with rendered finish
M22 Sprayed mineral fibre coatings
M23 Resin bound mineral coatings

M30 Metal mesh lathing/Anchored reinforcement for plastered coatings
M31 Fibrous plaster

M40 Stone/Concrete/Quarry/Ceramic tiling/Mosaic
M41 Terrazzo tiling/In situ terrazzo
M42 Wood block/Composition block/Parquet flooring

(continued)

M50 Rubber/Plastics/Cork/Lino/Carpet tiling/sheeting
M51 Edge fixed carpeting
M52 Decorative papers/fabrics

M60 Painting/Clear finishing

N Furniture/Equipment

N10 General fixtures/furnishings/equipment
N11 Domestic kitchen fittings
N12 Catering equipment
N13 Sanitary appliances/fittings
N14 Interior landscape
N15 Signs/Notices

N20)
N21) Appropriate section titles for each project
N22)
N23)

P Building fabric sundries

P10 Sundry insulation/proofing work/fire stops
P11 Foamed/Fibre/Bead cavity wall insulation

P20 Unframed isolated trims/skirtings/sundry items
P21 Ironmongery
P22 Sealant joints

P30 Trenches/Pipeways/Pits for buried engineering services
P31 Holes/Chases/Covers/Supports for services

Q Paving/Planting/Fencing/Site furniture

Q10 Stone/Concrete/Brick kerbs/edgings/channels

Q20 Hardcore/Granular/Cement bound bases/sub-bases to roads/pavings
Q21 In situ concrete roads/pavings/bases
Q22 Coated macadam/Asphalt roads/pavings
Q23 Gravel/Hoggin roads/pavings
Q24 Interlocking brick/block roads/pavings
Q25 Slab/Brick/Sett/Cobble pavings
Q26 Special surfacings/pavings for sport

Q30 Seeding/Turfing
Q31 Planting

Q40 Fencing

Q50 Site/Street furniture/equipment

R Disposal systems

R10 Rainwater pipework/gutters
R11 Foul drainage above ground
R12 Drainage below ground
R13 Land drainage
R14 Laboratory/Industrial waste drainage

R20 Sewage pumping
R21 Sewage treatment/sterilisation

R30 Centralised vacuum cleaning
R31 Refuse chutes
R32 Compactors/Macerators
R33 Incineration plant

S Piped supply systems

S10 Cold water
S11 Hot water
S12 Hot and cold water (small scale)
S13 Pressurised water
S14 Irrigation
S15 Fountains/Water features

S20 Treated/Deionised/Distilled water
S21 Swimming pool water treatment

S30 Compressed air
S31 Instrument air

(continued)

S32 Natural gas
S33 Liquid petroleum gas
S34 Medical/Laboratory gas

S40 Petrol/Oil – lubrication
S41 Fuel oil storage/distribution

S50 Vacuum
S51 Steam

S60 Fire hose reels
S61 Dry risers
S62 Wet risers
S63 Sprinklers
S64 Deluge
S65 Fire hydrants

S70 Gas fire fighting
S71 Foam fire fighting

T Mechanical heating/Cooling/Refrigeration systems

T10 Gas/Oil fired boilers
T11 Coal fired boilers
T12 Electrode/Direct electric boilers
T13 Packaged steam generators
T14 Heat pumps
T15 Solar collectors
T16 Alternative fuel boilers

T20 Primary heat distribution

T30 Medium temperature hot water heating
T31 Low temperature hot water heating
T32 Low temperature hot water heating (small scale)
T33 Steam heating

T40 Warm air heating
T41 Warm air heating (small scale)
T42 Local heating units

T50 Heat recovery

T60 Central refrigeration plant
T61 Primary/Secondary cooling distribution

T70 Local cooling units
T71 Cold rooms
T72 Ice pads

U Ventilation/Air conditioning systems

U10 General supply/extract
U11 Toilet extract
U12 Kitchen extract
U13 Car parking extract
U14 Smoke extract/Smoke control
U15 Safety cabinet/Fume cupboard extract
U16 Fume extract
U17 Anaesthetic gas extract

U20 Dust collection

U30 Low velocity air conditioning
U31 VAV air conditioning
U32 Dual-duct air conditioning
U33 Multi-zone air conditioning

U40 Induction air conditioning
U41 Fan-coil air conditioning
U42 Terminal re-heat air conditioning
U43 Terminal heat pump air conditioning

U50 Hybrid system air conditioning

U60 Free standing air conditioning units
U61 Window/Wall air conditioning units

U70 Air curtains

V Electrical supply/power/lighting systems

V10 Electricity generation plant
V11 HV supply/distribution/public utility supply
V12 LV supply/public utility supply

V20 LV distribution
V21 General lighting
V22 General LV power

V30 Extra low voltage supply
V31 DC supply
V32 Uninterrupted power supply

V40 Emergency lighting
V41 Street/Area/Flood lighting
V42 Studio/Auditorium/Arena lighting

V50 Electric underfloor heating
V51 Local electric heating units

V90 General lighting and power (small scale)

W Communications/Security/Control systems

W10 Telecommunications
W11 Staff paging/location
W12 Public address/Sound amplification
W13 Centralized dictation

W20 Radio/TV/CCTV
W21 Projection
W22 Advertising display
W23 Clocks

W30 Data transmission

W40 Access control
W41 Security detection and alarm

W50 Fire detection and alarm
W51 Earthing and bonding
W52 Lightning protection
W53 Electromagnetic screening

W60 Monitoring
W61 Central control
W62 Building automation

X Transport systems

X10 Lifts
X11 Escalators
X12 Moving pavements

X20 Hoists
X21 Cranes
X22 Travelling cradles
X23 Goods distribution/Mechanised warehousing

X30 Mechanical document conveying
X31 Pneumatic document conveying
X32 Automatic document filing and retrieval

Y Services reference specification

Y10 Pipelines
Y11 Pipeline ancillaries

Y20 Pumps
Y21 Water tanks/cisterns
Y22 Heat exchangers
Y23 Storage cylinders/calorifiers
Y24 Trace heating
Y25 Cleaning and chemical treatment

Y30 Air ductlines
Y31 Air ductline ancillaries

Y40 Air handling units
Y41 Fans
Y42 Air filtration
Y43 Heating/Cooling coils
Y44 Humidifiers
Y45 Silencers/Acoustic treatment
Y46 Grilles/Diffusers/Louvres

Y50 Thermal insulation
Y51 Testing and commissioning of mechanical services
Y52 Vibration isolation mountings
Y53 Control components – mechanical
Y54 Identification – mechanical
Y59 Sundry common mechanical items

Y60 Conduit and cable trunking
Y61 HV/LV cables and wiring
Y62 Busbar trunking
Y63 Support components – cables

Y70 HV switchgear
Y71 LV switchgear and distribution boards
Y72 Contactors and starters
Y73 Luminaires and lamps
Y74 Accessories for electrical services

Y80 Earthing and bonding components
Y81 Testing and commissioning of electrical services
Y82 Identification – electrical
Y89 Sundry common electrical items

Y90 Fixing to building fabric
Y91 Off-site painting/Anti-corrosion treatments
Y92 Motor drives – electric

Z Building fabric reference specification

Z10 Purpose made joinery
Z11 Purpose made metalwork

Z20 Fixings/Adhesives
Z21 Mortars
Z22 Sealants

Z30 Off-site painting

Example work section definitions

K12
Under purlin/Inside rail panel linings

Manufactured boards and rigid flat sheets fixed as a complete system with proprietary edge supports and jointing sections under the roof purlins or inside the cladding rails of framed buildings.

Included

Rigid sheets of the following materials and fixing as a complete lining system under purlins and inside rails:
- Plywood
- Chipboard
- Medium board
- Mineral fibre board
- Gypsum plastics faced board
- Vermiculite boards
- Boards/sheets of other materials
- Veneered and faced boards

Proprietary edge supports, jointing sections and fixings

Trimming and finishing around columns, beams and openings with proprietary trim

Cutting holes and openings other than for engineering services

Excluded

General timber or metal supports
(Relevant section, e.g. G10, G12, G20)

Edge supported/Reinforced woodwool slab decking, G32

Rigid sheet cladding, H20

Wall/ceiling lining systems, over purlin/outside rail
(Relevant profiled sheet cladding section, H30, H31)

Plasterboard dry lining, K10

Rigid sheet flooring/sheathing/linings/casings, K11

Suspended ceilings, K40

Plasterboard backings for plaster
(Plastered/Rendered/Roughcast coatings, M20)

Site decoration
(Painting/Clear finishing, M60)

Holes for pipes
(Holes/Chases/Covers/Supports for services, P31)

Q22
Coated macadam/Asphalt roads/pavings

Roads, paths, pavings and surfacings of mastic asphalt, rolled asphalt, or tar or bitumen coated aggregate.

Included

Coated macadam roadbases

Base courses and/or wearing courses of:
- Tarmacadam
- Dense tarmacadam
- Bitumen macadam
- Hot rolled asphalt
- Fine cold (rolled) asphalt
- Dense tar surfacing
- Mastic asphalt

Dressings of rock, gravel or pre-coated chippings

Application of binder

Repairing and resurfacing existing pavings

Rolling surfaces of roadbases, base courses, wearing courses, surface dressings, etc.

Forming channels, gutters, etc.

Separating membranes

Preservative treated timber edgings and pegs

Jointing to existing or other work

Making good around standards, bollards, covers, gulleys, etc.

Excluded

Surfacings of paving asphalt to multi-storey car parks
(Mastic asphalt roofing/insulation/finishes, J21)

Mastic asphalt flooring, M11

Stone/Concrete/Brick kerbs/edgings/channels, Q10

Hardcore/Granular/Cement bound bases/sub-bases to roads/pavings, Q20

In situ concrete bases
(In situ concrete roads/pavings/bases, Q21)

S63
Sprinklers

A pipework distribution system charged with water, with a network of heat sensitive sprinkler heads. Should the temperature rise above a critical point the sprinkler head will actuate and a water spray will be emitted.

Included

Reference specification items

Pipelines, Y10

Pipeline ancillaries, Y11

Pumps, Y20

Water tanks/cisterns, Y21

Trace heating, Y24

Cleaning and chemical treatment, Y25

Thermal insulation, Y50

Testing and commissioning of mechanical services, Y51

Vibration isolation mountings, Y52

Control components – mechanical, Y53

Identification-mechanical, Y54

Sundry common mechanical items, Y59

Contactors and starters, Y72

Fixing to building fabric, Y90

Off site painting and anti-corrosion treatments, Y91

Motor drives-electric, Y92

Particular specification items

Reaction and control devices

Sprinkler heads

Internal combustion engine drives and fuel systems

Excluded

LV distribution, V20

Fire detection and alarm, W50

Central control, W61

Builder's work including concrete tanks
(Various sections)

Production Drawings Code

Generally

The technical content of specifications and quantities can be regulated by and taken from standard documents to a fairly high degree – SMM7, NBS, NES and BQ phrase libraries are obvious examples. But this is not true of production drawings – the shapes, dimensions, junctions and features which they show are infinitely variable project to project, so that only a minority of the information can be drawn from standard conventions. Therefore, the Code for Production Drawings does not include long checklists or libraries of data, so it is much smaller than the conventions for specification and measurement.

The Code gives advice in relation to:

1. Arrangement and presentation of drawings, including information structuring, sheet sizes, scales, annotation, titling and numbering.
2. Procedures for co-ordinating the content of drawings, planning their production, and producing them efficiently and effectively.

The Common arrangement

The 'Common arrangement of work sections' (see pages 8 to 13) has been developed to perform a major co-ordinating role, so what relevance does it have to drawings practice?

A certain 'approximateness' has to be accepted in the classification of drawings. Thus a drawing titled 'Roof' is unlikely to show every last bit of information about the roof, nor will it show just the roof, for the relationships with adjacent elements and types of work are of central importance. It follows that if drawings were to be arranged by CAWS the common titling between drawings, specification and quantities would be misleading, for the content of the drawings would almost certainly not coincide with the corresponding sections of the specification and quantities.

If 'work section' sets of drawings were to be prepared, most junctions in the building would be drawn several times, each from a different point of view. The result would be vastly to increase the number of drawings without corresponding advantage. It is clearly better for such 'general' or 'relationships' drawings to be produced once only, and to be used several times by different trades.

Therefore CAWS is not recommended for the arrangement of drawings. Nevertheless co-ordination can be achieved by consistent cross-referencing to the specification in the annotation of drawings e.g.

Concrete mix E10/104
Lead flashing H71
Post and rail fence Q40/260
Booster fan U33/230

Such code references will also be helpful in finding information in the bills of quantities.

To enable such specific clause references to be given, the specification will need to be prepared in good time. If it is not available, so that the clause numbers are not known, co-ordination may be achieved by CAWS section numbers and careful use of terminology.

Arrangement

The essence of good arrangement is the division of the whole set of production drawings into easily recognised groups.

There is no single 'best' arrangement for drawings which applies to all projects. Many factors such as size and complexity of project and types of construction need to be taken into account. The most effective arrangement will result from giving the right emphasis to each factor for the particular circumstances of each project design. Where an office wishes to adopt a standard arrangement for all or a portion of its workload, a careful assessment of the nature of the included projects will need to be made.

Grouping of drawings may be any combination of the following:

- Office of origin, i.e. architectural, structural and services drawings.
- Type of information, i.e.
  L = Location drawings (plan, section, elevation)
  S = Schedules (a special type of location drawing)
  A = Assembly drawings
  C = Component drawings
  (References to A and C drawings are given on the L and S drawings)
- Parts of the building, e.g. frame, walls, roof, windows, finishes, heating installation, security installation. These may include parts constructed by specialist firms, e.g. piling, suspended ceilings. A standard list of elements may be used.
- Location, e.g. blocks, zones, house types, levels.

The Code gives detailed advice on the arrangement of drawings for all sizes of project and gives a fully explained example. Considerable emphasis is placed on avoiding unnecessary and unhelpful fragmentation of the information.

Format and presentation

The Code for Production Drawings is complementary to BS 1192:Part 1:1984 'Construction drawing practice', which should be read in conjunction.

The Code gives detailed advice on the following:

- Sheet sizes – the pros and cons of A0, A1, A2, A3 and A4 sizes and combinations thereof.
- Scales – the principles which should influence choice of scales, e.g. the avoidance of too small a scale for location drawings and too large a scale for details, in order to avoid the need for intermediate scale drawings.
- Drawing numbers – the use of blocks of numbers, mnemonic letters, elemental codes, etc: the importance of not letting the coding system cause over-fragmentation of the drawings set.
- Drawings titles – the importance of accurate and helpful titles.

Co-ordinating the information

Figure C on page 5 is a breakdown by type and effect of 700 clashes between drawings identified during a BRE Survey of 25 building sites. It shows that two thirds of the clashes involved services or provision of space or holes for services. The Code gives extensive guidance on the techniques and procedures which should be followed by architects and engineers in order to minimise the incidence of such problems, e.g.

- Careful consideration at design stage of space requirements and zoning for services.
- Good communication within the design team, e.g. to ensure that only up to date drawings are used.
- Good management of drawings preparation, e.g. copy negatives should be taken at the optimum time, and amendments should be closely controlled and recorded.
- Use of overlay checking or combined services drawings in order to eliminate conflicts.
- Production of detailed drawings where the space for services is limited and where several services occur in close proximity, e.g. ducts, ceiling voids.

Planning the preparation

Recognising the desirability of providing a complete or virtually complete set of drawings before tender action, the Code recommends that much attention should be given to planning and management of drawings production. A suggested procedure is set out in considerable detail, including:

- Checking the completeness of the design and co-ordination of services and structure.
- Making an initial appraisal of the size of the task and the resources which will be required.
- Determining the arrangement and presentation of the drawings set (as described above).
- Making a firm allocation of resources, so that the draughtsmen can be involved in the finalisation of the plan.
- Preparing a schedule of drawings (see Figure D), definitions of the purpose and content of each

PROJECT : PROJECT No :

Drawing no	Title	Scale	Sheet size	Man days	Notes

Figure D
Schedule of drawings – prepared before drafting starts

Figure E
Definitions of purpose and content can be in the form of miniature cartoons

drawing (see Figure E) and a plan for use of copy negatives (see Figure F).

- Assessing the man-hours required to gather necessary information and produce each drawing. On the basis of this preparing a drawings programme (see Figure G).
- Monitoring the production of the drawings against the programme.

Each design discipline should plan the production of its own drawings on the lines set out above and in the context of an overall design team programme (see Figure H).

CAD and overlay draughting

A major benefit of computer drafting and overlay draughting is that information can be prepared and stored in 'layers' which can then be printed in different combinations. This enables drawings to be prepared without the use of copy negatives and avoids repetitive draughting. Perhaps most important of all, provided the 'layering' is carefully planned, CAD and overlay draughting permit the desirable combinations of information to be chosen retrospectively, avoiding the need to forecast them in a copy negative production plan (see Figure F).

Revision and issue

The Code recommends the preparation and subsequent updating of a drawings register for issue to all users. Checklists should be used to ensure that everyone who needs a particular drawing is issued with a copy.

All drawings affected by a revision should be brought up to date promptly. Revisions should be identified by description and, if practicable, by graphic means. Whenever new or revised drawings are issued they should be accompanied by a confirmation sheet, a copy of this being kept for record purposes.

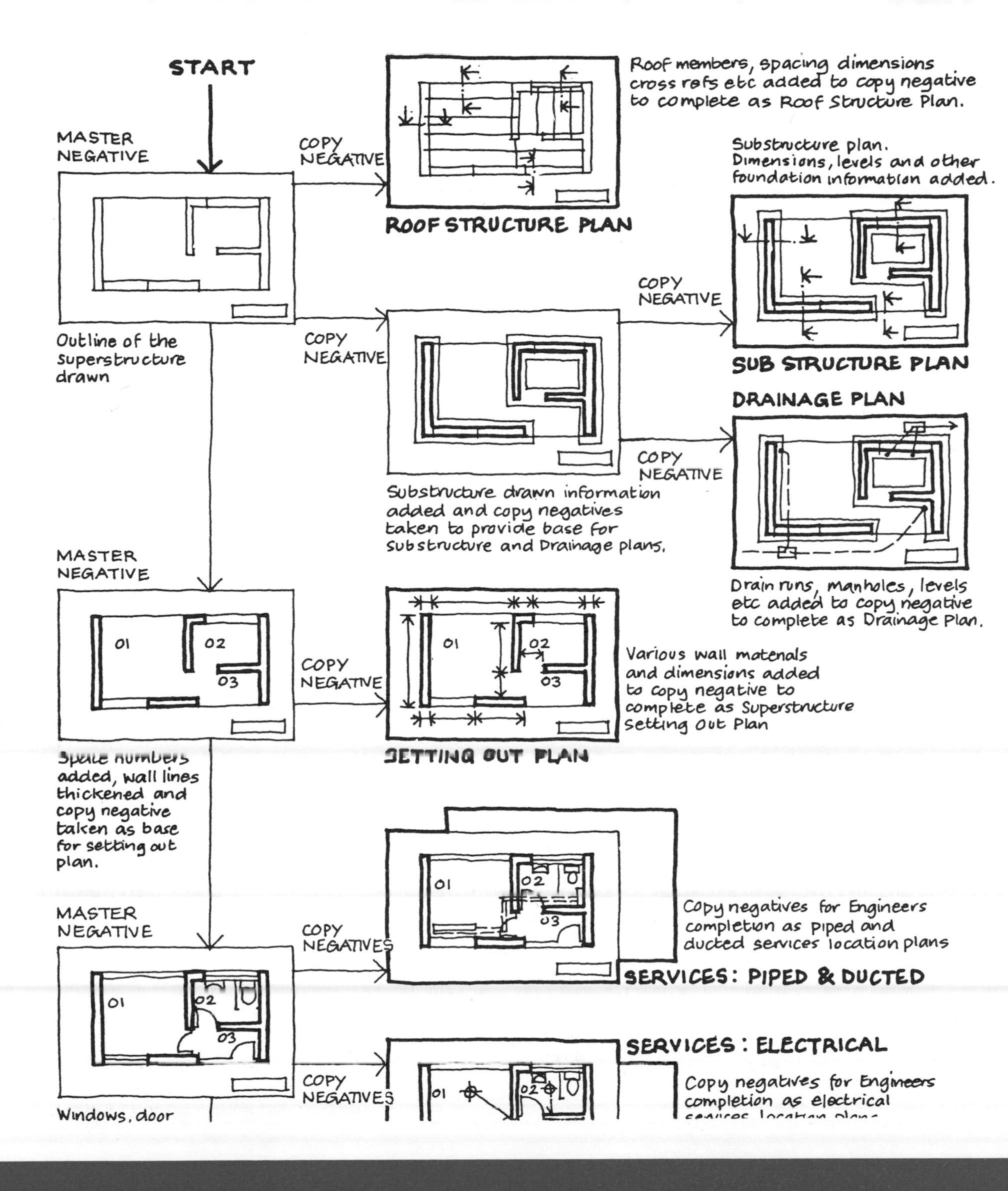
START
MASTER
NEGATIVE
COPY
NEGATIVE
Roof members, spacing dimensions cross refs etc added to copy negative to complete as Roof Structure Plan.
ROOF STRUCTURE PLAN
Substructure plan. Dimensions, levels and other foundation information added.
Outline of the superstructure drawn
COPY
NEGATIVE
COPY
NEGATIVE
SUB STRUCTURE PLAN
DRAINAGE PLAN
COPY
NEGATIVE
Substructure drawn information added and copy negatives taken to provide base for substructure and Drainage plans.
MASTER
NEGATIVE
Drain runs, manholes, levels etc added to copy negative to complete as Drainage Plan.
01
02
03
COPY
NEGATIVE
Various wall materials and dimensions added to copy negative to complete as Superstructure Setting Out Plan
SETTING OUT PLAN
Space numbers added, wall lines thickened and copy negative taken as base for setting out plan.
Copy negatives for Engineers completion as piped and ducted services location plans
MASTER
NEGATIVE
COPY
NEGATIVES
SERVICES: PIPED & DUCTED
SERVICES: ELECTRICAL
COPY
NEGATIVES
Copy negatives for Engineers completion as electrical
Windows, door

Figure F
Copy negative drawings production plan

The building outlines, etc. shown on the drawings in the illustration would not, in practice, be shown. They have been included to aid understanding of the illustration.

Figure G A drawings programme

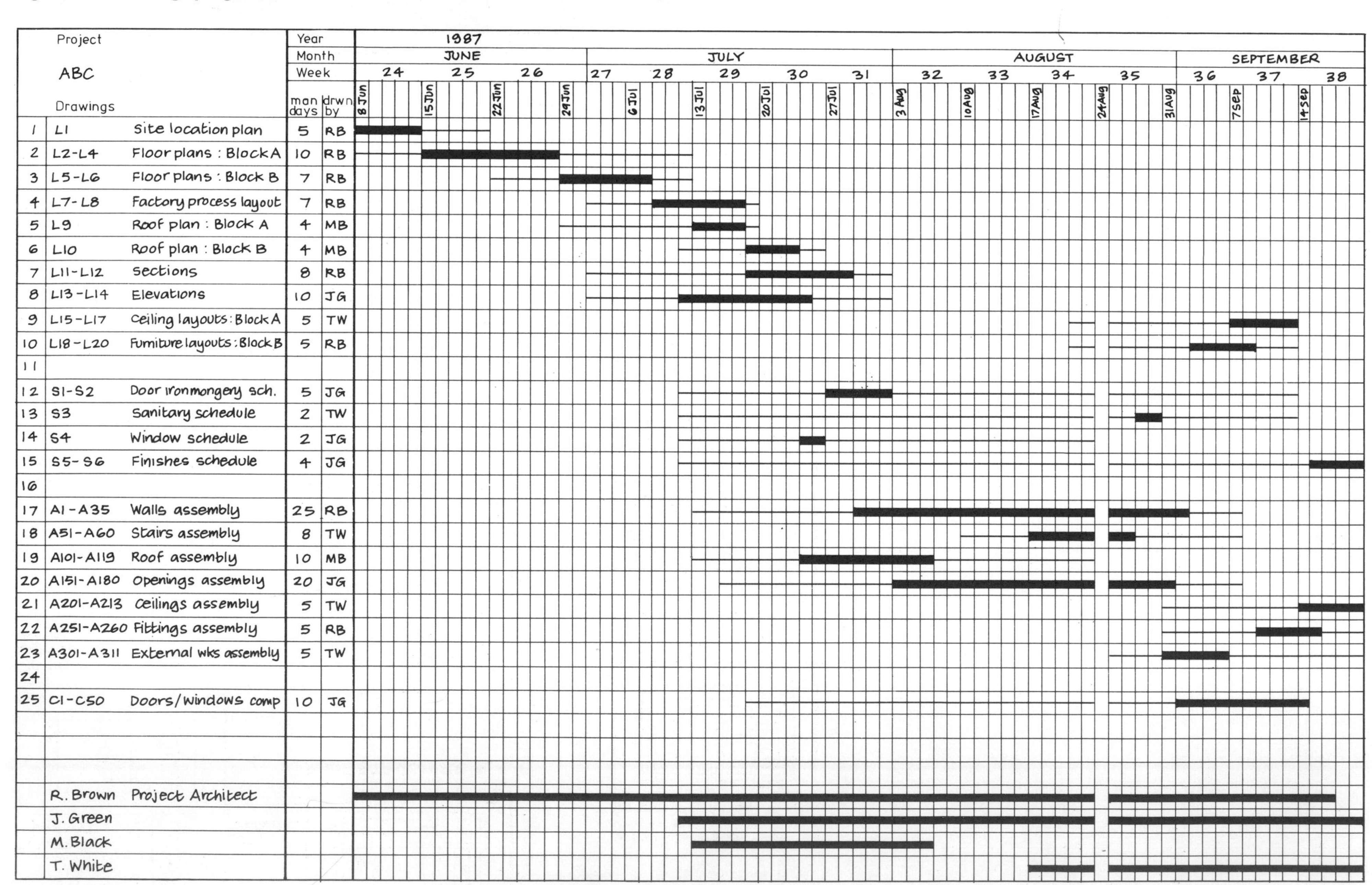

Project
ABC
Drawings
Year
Month
Week
1987
JUNE
JULY
AUGUST
SEPTEMBER
24 25 26 27 28 29 30 31 32 33 34 35 36 37 38
man days
drwn by
8 Jun
15 Jun
22 Jun
29 Jun
6 Jul
13 Jul
20 Jul
27 Jul
3 Aug
10 Aug
17 Aug
24 Aug
31 Aug
7 Sep
14 Sep
1 L1 Site location plan 5 RB
2 L2-L4 Floor plans : Block A 10 RB
3 L5-L6 Floor plans : Block B 7 RB
4 L7-L8 Factory process layout 7 RB
5 L9 Roof plan : Block A 4 MB
6 L10 Roof plan : Block B 4 MB
7 L11-L12 Sections 8 RB
8 L13-L14 Elevations 10 JG
9 L15-L17 Ceiling layouts : Block A 5 TW
10 L18-L20 Furniture layouts : Block B 5 RB
11
12 S1-S2 Door ironmongery sch. 5 JG
13 S3 Sanitary schedule 2 TW
14 S4 Window schedule 2 JG
15 S5-S6 Finishes schedule 4 JG
16
17 A1-A35 Walls assembly 25 RB
18 A51-A60 Stairs assembly 8 TW
19 A101-A119 Roof assembly 10 MB
20 A151-A180 Openings assembly 20 JG
21 A201-A213 Ceilings assembly 5 TW
22 A251-A260 Fittings assembly 5 RB
23 A301-A311 External wks assembly 5 TW
24
25 C1-C50 Doors/windows comp 10 JG
R. Brown Project Architect
J. Green
M. Black
T. White

Figure H Overall design team programme

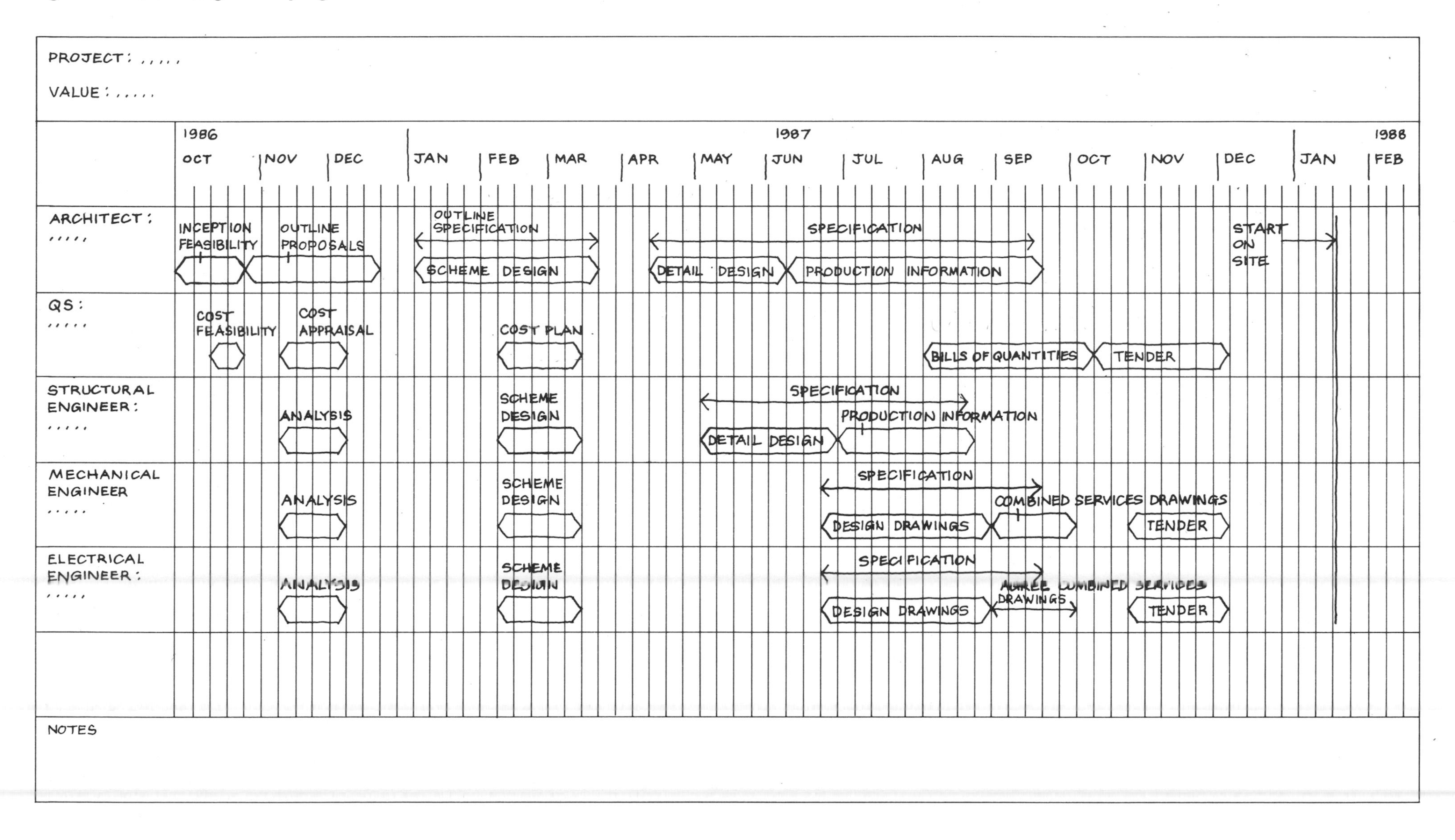

The programme illustrates a conventional procedure, but the principles of CPI are equally relevant to accelerated procedures such as management contracting.

Project Specification Code

Of the three basic types of project documentation, specification (often called preambles) has lagged furthest behind in terms of quality and helpfulness. The Project Specification Code will help practitioners to review and upgrade their specification practice in order that the potential value of the specification as an aid to pricing and quality control can be realised.

Significant improvement is sought so that in the future project specifications will be:

- Comprehensive, covering every significant aspect of quality.
- Produced specifically for each project, with no irrelevant material.
- Appropriate having regard to the nature of the project and the available knowledge, resources and means of verification.
- Practicable, requirements being specified only if this can be demonstrated. Once specified, requirements should be enforced.
- Constructive, in other words helpfully specific, so that all parties know what is expected of them.
- Up to date, reflecting current good building practice and the most recent published industry standards.
- Clearly and economically worded.

The Code is divided into three parts:

A. General principles of specification writing.
B. Guidance on coverage.
C. Illustration of use of libraries of clauses.

. . . arranged so that the contents can be co-related speedily and certainly with the drawings, quantities and schedules . . .

Part A
General principles of specification writing

Co-ordination between documents

Specification information can be given on drawings, in measured items or schedules of work as well as in the project specification. To minimise repetition and discrepancies, and to give greater certainty as to the location of information, it is recommended that full specification is normally given only in the project specification. Drawings, quantities and schedules of work should then identify the various kinds and qualities of work by using a few carefully chosen words with, as appropriate, a reference to the relevant clause(s) in the specification.

On JCT With Quantities contracts the specification should be given the status of a Contract Document by incorporating it into the bills of quantities. It may appear as a separate bill e.g. 'Bill 2 Specification' or be divided up as specification preambles to the various sections of measured work.

Arrangement of the specification

The project specification should be arranged by CAWS (see pages 8 to 13). The internal arrangement of the work sections should be designed so that the contents can be co-related speedily and certainly with the drawings, quantities and schedules. The arrangement of clauses into 'Materials' and 'Workmanship' is not recommended where it would involve separate drawings or bill cross-references for materials, accessories and workmanship. Composite descriptions i.e. 'type of work items' and combined materials/workmanship clauses are recommended wherever their use is practicable (see example specifications on pages 40 to 51).

Performance or prescription

In the past there has been much theorising about this, but for the practitioner the question is dominated by practical limitations. With performance specification these include the difficulty of defining subjective requirements, doubts about the contractor's skill and knowledge, the high cost of tendering and, not least, verification. Prescriptive specification can also present problems, e.g. is the designer's requirement the most practical and economic solution, and can it be verified that it has been provided? The best available means of controlling quality will often be a mixture of performance and prescription specification. The two can usually be combined successfully provided the specifier has sufficient knowledge and skill to avoid practical conflicts. The blend will vary from one type of work to another.

Options and alternatives

The Code recommends that wherever design priorities allow the specification should permit options and alternatives. Products and materials may be specified by reference to a standard, by listing alternative manufacturers or by stating *'. . . or equivalent of approved appearance/colour/design/ etc'.* Choice of sub-contractors and manufacturers of purpose made components may be left to the contractor or a list of acceptable firms given.

Reference or description

Specification by reference to other documents can save much time for both specifiers and contractors. But at the same time there is much bad practice, notably the use of blanket references to Codes of Practice which the specifier has not read and the contractor will not have on site. Before referring to a document it is good practice to review its relevance, currency and whether it is couched in clear instructional terms. Acquisition of documents can be costly and time consuming for the contractor, so it is unhelpful to invoke just a small part of a substantial document. References should be helpfully precise, identifying the part, clause, type, grade or other designations which apply.

Variations of approach

The approach to specification needs to vary from one type of work to another, depending on several factors including:

- Whether the materials and components are standard or purpose-made.
- The extreme variability of industry documents, both 'official' and proprietary.
- The relative state of knowledge between the designer and the specialist trade or sub-contractor.
- The available methods of verification.

The Code provides a useful detailed discussion, with examples.

Small works – the need for brevity

The Code recognises the need for small works specifications to be brief, but points out that in the past they have often been excessively so. There is a strong case for increasing the technical content, but the Code suggests that this increase should be concentrated on those sections of the project which have a particular cost and/or quality significance.

Brevity can be achieved by:

- Excluding minor types of work from the specification, covering them by brief notes on the drawings or in the schedule of work.
- Specifying standard rather than purpose-made components and assemblies – the latter involve much more substantial specification.
- Specifying in a more general, less specifically detailed way, and leaving out clauses of marginal relevance.

Such specifications may define the quality of work in a less precise and comprehensive way. Other aspects of quality control should therefore be considered even more carefully, including the quality of the drawings and/or schedule of work and selection of reliable contractors.

Producing the specification

The specification should be prepared by the design office(s) involved in the project, care being taken to co-ordinate the contents of the various sections. The writing of the specification should not be left to the quantity surveyor although he, as first user of the draft document, can perform an invaluable checking role.

Preparation of a specification requires knowledge of and/or reference to an enormous amount of technical information. To cope with this, the design office should encourage individuals within the office to develop expertise on certain topics, operate an efficient technical library (preferably selective) and maintain a suitable up-to-date library of specification clauses (see pages 24 and 25).

The Code sets out a model procedure as follows:

- Prepare the specification early, either before or in parallel with the production drawings.
- Undertake the necessary technical research for each section first, and be aware that this may be time consuming.
- Record decisions as they are taken by marking up a copy of the library of clauses.
- On completion check that each section is complete and appropriate to the project.
- On with quantities jobs supply the specification to the quantity surveyor in draft form subject by subject to match the supply of drawings.

Finally, the Code gives recommendations on word processing, proof reading, page breaks, indexing, number of copies, etc.

Part B
Guidance on coverage

This is the most substantial part of the Code and consists of checklists for a wide range of building fabric and services work sections: see Figures J and K.

The degree of detail to be given against each item is at the discretion of the designer. Items which do not apply to the particular project should, of course, be disregarded. Conversely , if the project design calls for important specification information not covered by the checklists, this should be provided. The checklists give typical clause headings but do not necessarily give sub-headings which might appear within clauses. For example in section H31 the item for basic joints does not mention particular requirements for mortar, e.g. special sand, or pigment.

H51

Natural stone slab cladding/ features

General requirements

Where contractor design is required:
  Information to be submitted at tender stage
  Information to be submitted before production

Tolerances/accuracy of cladding

Performance requirements:
  Wind and other loads
  Weather resistance
  Accommodation of thermal and moisture movements

Selection of stone for freedom from defects

Cutting of stone:
  Minimum thicknesses
  Accuracy
  Stones left oversize for site cutting

Handling, storing and protecting stone

Fixing methods and procedures

Control samples

Requirements for each type of cladding

Type and source of stone, and finish

Types of fixing, type and grade of metal

Width and filling for basic joints

Width and filling for movement joints

Cavity insulation

Accessories (copings, cills, dpcs, flashings, etc)

Figure J
A building fabric specification checklist
(Courtesy of NBS Ltd)

S11
Hot water

Refer to reference specification checklists

Y10 Pipelines
Y11 Pipeline ancillaries
Y20 Pumps
Y22 Heat exchangers
Y23 Storage cylinders/calorifiers
Y25 Cleaning and chemical treatment
Y51 Testing and commissioning of mechanical services
Y52 Vibration isolation mountings
Y53 Control components - mechanical
Y54 Identification - mechanical
Y90 Fixing to building fabric
Y91 Off site painting/Anti-corrosion treatments
Y92 Motor drives - electric

Products/Materials specific to this section

Heated towel rails
Local direct water heaters

Workmanship specific to this section

Heated towel rail installation
Connections to taps and appliances
Local water heater installation

Y52

Vibration isolation mountings

General

Design intent
Spring anti vibration mountings
Spring hangers
Locking facility

Products/Materials

Mountings
Hangers
Inertia bases
Vibration isolation hoses
Pipework vibration isolation
Pipe wall and riser seals

Workmanship

Cast in situ bases
Fixing
Horizontally restrained spring mountings

Figure K
Building services specification checklists
(Courtesy of NES Ltd)

Part C
Libraries of specification clauses

Specification writing from scratch is very time consuming, and there are obvious technical and economic advantages in using sound clauses repeatedly, adapting them only where special circumstances apply. The Code recommends good quality 'libraries' of clauses, with guidance notes, as the only practicable way of coping with the constantly changing mass of specification information. The Code lists the criteria with which libraries of clauses should comply.

General use of commercially available libraries of clauses is envisaged. Such libraries may be used for the direct production of project specifications or as the basis for an 'office' library of clauses. A third alternative is to use the commercial library direct, but to create a set of additional office guidance notes giving preferred products, practices to be avoided, suggested text for supplementary clauses, etc.

The National Building Specification (sponsored by the RIBA) and the National Engineering Specification (sponsored by CIBSE) have been produced to meet this need. If they are used it should not be necessary to use the checklists in Part B of the Code.

Natural stone slab cladding/features (continued) **H51**

370
These sample fixings will make it easier to check different types of fixings which may be similar in appearance. The samples should be kept on site in the Clerk of Work's office.

370 SAMPLES OF FIXINGS: submit a sample of each type of fixing, including shims, clearly identified and with manufacturer's recommended torque figures and shim dimensions.

380
Close supervision on site is important. The first thing to check is that the actual fixings specified are in fact used, and in the correct place. The high cost of most fixings can be a temptation to employ cheaper substitutes or for fixings to be missed out. The non-ferrous materials have a high scrap value, but stainless steel does not and is therefore less prone to theft.

Loadbearing fixings are more critical than restraint fixings. When threaded bolt fixings are used it is recommended that the torque figure is checked on a random basis using a calibrated torque spanner (which in turn should be checked weekly). For each fixing manufacturers recommend a torque figure and a limit for the dimension which can be packed out using shims. Check that these have not been exceeded and that any shims used are of the correct material and size.

The prohibition of mortar spacer dabs in external cladding may be regarded as an unconventional requirement. See general guidance notes for 'Restraint fixings' on page 4.

Delete the last sub-item if not required. Insert e.g. *'every other'* or *'every third'*.

380 FIXING:
- Do not exceed the torque figures or shim dimensions recommended by the manufacturer.
- Grout dowel bars with a fairly dry 1:4 cement:sand mix or a suitable epoxy or polyester mix, well tamped in.
- In external cladding do not use mortar spacer dabs and keep cavity completely free of mortar and other debris.
- Give reasonable notice to CA to allow inspection to take place before covering up loadbearing fixings.
- Give reasonable notice to CA of the completion of _ _ _ _ _ _ _ _ _ _ stone course to allow inspection of restraint fixings and cavity before proceeding with the next course.

390 INSULATION: ensure that insulation is firmly held against the backing wall with close butt joints accurately cut to lines of stone fixings. Trim edges neatly and accurately around fixings.

BASIC JOINTS

See general guidance notes on pages 4 and 5 and type items on pages 7 and 8.

410, 420
Alternative clauses for use with sandstones and limestones. The two clauses represent alternative ways of obtaining a matching colour.

410 BASIC JOINTS (MORTAR FILLED):
- Mortar mix:
  - 1 part ordinary Portland cement
  - 2 parts lime putty, ready prepared to BS 890
  - 8-9 parts matching crushed stone sand passing a 1.4 mm sieve
- Thoroughly wet stones, fully butter vertical joints, lay on a full bed, ensure that excess mortar does not fall into cavity and finish joints flush as the work proceeds.
- Wood or plastic joint spacers may be used but remove and make good to match as soon as mortar has set.

...(MORTAR FILLED):

Figure L
A page from NBS

Copyright NES Ltd January 1987 **Y10 Pipelines**

2260, 2270, 2280, 2290 Copper to BS 2871 Part 1 class W, X, Y and Z

Copper tubes primarily used for water, but also used for gas and sanitation applications.

Suitable for connection by capillary or compression fittings

Class W :- annealed; suitable for micro-bore or mini-bore heating systems

Class X :- half hard, light gauge; suitable for hot and cold water

Class Y :- half hard or annealed; suitable for burying underground

Class Z :- hard drawn, thin wall; suitable for hot and cold water, but not recommended for bending or manipulation

For low temperature hot water heating - use class W,X,Y or Z. For domestic hot and cold water, chilled and cooling water - use X,Y or Z

Special cleaning of copper pipe as indicated.

2260 COPPER TO BS 2871 PART 1, CLASS W

Material : Copper, Class W
Standard : BS 2871
Dimensions : BS 2871 Part 1, table W
* preferred thickness
* other recommended thickness
Ends : Plain
Finish
* Uncoated
* Sheathed in white polyethylene
* Sheathed in profiled white polyethylene

2270 COPPER TO BS 2871 PART 1, CLASS X

Material : Copper, Class X
Standard : BS 2871
Dimensions : BS 2871 Part 1, table X
Ends : Plain
Finish
* Uncoated
* Degreased
* Sheathed in white polyethylene
* Sheathed in profiled white polyethylene
* Sheathed in green polyethylene
* Sheathed in yellow ochre polyethylene
* Nickel plated
* Chromium plated
* Tinned inside and outside with pure tin
* Tinned outside with pure tin

2280 COPPER TO BS 2871 PART 1, CLASS Y

Material : Copper, Class Y
Standard
* BS 2871, half hard
* BS 2871, annealed
Dimensions : BS 2871 Part 1, table Y
Ends : Plain
Finish
* Uncoated
* Sheathed in white polyethylene
* Sheathed in profiled white polyethylene
* Sheathed in green polyethylene
* Nickel plated
* Chromium plated
* Tinned inside and outside with pure tin
* Tinned outside with pure tin

2290 COPPER TO BS 2871 PART 1, CLASS Z

Material : Copper, Class Z
Standard : BS 2871
BS 2871 Part 1, table Z

Figure M
A page from NES

SMM7 Standard Method of Measurement of Building Works

Unlike the other co-ordinated conventions described in this Guide, SMM has a long history. It was first published in 1922, has been referred to in the RIBA (now JCT) Form of Contract since 1931, and over the years has acquired a considerable standing.

The changes made in SMM7 are the result of an extremely thorough review. This started in 1971 with the report of the Joint Working Party on Measurement Conventions, since when there has been virtually continuous work by the SMM Development Unit or the SMM Standing Joint Committee. SMM6, published in 1979, was regarded as an interim revision, so SMM7 can be seen as the culmination of 16 years' work.

Bringing SMM up to date

In the past there has been a certain unevenness in the technical coverage of SMM so that, for example, SMM6 has four pages of rules for rubble walling, but none for grp cladding or raised access floors. SMM7 includes rules for virtually every type of building and services work in common use.

In contrast with the traditional prose style of previous editions, SMM7 adopts a tabular format (see Figure N) which is quicker and more systematic to use, and should make the document more easily understood.

However, updating the technical coverage and presenting the rules in a more modern style are not the main reasons for producing SMM7. The main objective of the new edition is to bring about a considerable simplification of bills of quantities.

The main problem

The first part of this Guide (pages 2 to 6) describes the problem of inadequate project information and how it affects the quality of building work. Poor or late information has similar detrimental effects on the cost of building, partly because of directly attributable delays, and partly because the time which site managers spend sorting out information problems is usually time that would have been more profitably spent organising and controlling the efficient execution of the work.

Despite the cost significance of the production information, it is not normal practice on with quantities projects to reveal to the contractor at tender stage the true state of completeness of the drawings. The production information for most projects is partly complete and partly incomplete at the time of seeking tenders. A competent quantity surveyor, particularly when working with an architect known to him and using his imagination as necessary, can produce from the minimum of information a bill of quantities that creates the illusion of a fully detailed and fully specified design. In general it is difficult for the contractor to distinguish the firm parts of bills from the fictional parts.

The complexity of bills of quantities

The problem bears hard on sub-contractors, for whilst main contractors may to an extent rely on a swings and roundabouts effect, the whole of one specialist type of work may be less than adequately described, placing the specialist sub-contractor at risk. For this reason most specialist sub-contractors prefer rules which require measurement of many sundry labours and features, so that in the absence of drawings they can gauge the complexity of the work and have some safeguard against the effects of post-contract variations.

SMM5 included detailed rules, resulting in bills of quantities with a large proportion of low cost sundry items. The rules were to a certain extent simplified in SMM6. Nevertheless the effect has been to 'draw a picture' in measured items – how much easier and more effective it would be for the contractor to assess the complexity of the work by inspecting the relevant drawings.

Consequently simplification of the rules has been the first priority in producing SMM7 so that measurement can be carried out more quickly, the number of items in bills of quantities being reduced significantly. At the same time the use of the rules is conditional upon the provision to contractors at tender stage of a certain minimum amount of drawn and specified information, in order that they can assess the complexity and required quality of the work. Provided this information is passed on to the specialist sub-contractors (and it is an all important proviso), the specialists' problems referred to above will be significantly reduced.

Provision of Drawings

The SMM7 rules for Preliminaries/General conditions require the provision of location drawings as follows:

- Block plan showing the site and proposed construction in relation to the surroundings.
- Site plan showing the position of the buildings in relation to the setting out point, the means of access and boundaries of the site.
- Plans, sections and elevations showing the position of the various spaces in the building and the general construction and location of the principal elements.

The rules for particular work sections require some supplementary drawn information, for example see Figure N. The requirements should be capable of being met by selection from drawings which are produced as a matter of course by the designers. Wherever practicable, reproduction of the relevant parts of the designers' drawings in the bill of quantities is suggested, in order to make life easier for the estimator.

Although the requirements for provision of drawn information are not onerous, they should not be taken lightly – they are a condition precedent to using the SMM7 rules at all. Of course the embargo

E20 Formwork for in situ concrete

Figure N Tabular format of SMM7 rules

INFORMATION PROVIDED					MEASUREMENT RULES	DEFINITION RULES	COVERAGE RULES	SUPPLEMENTARY INFORMATION
P1 The following information is shown either on location drawings under Work Group A Preliminaries/General conditions or on further drawings which accompany the bill of quantities: (a) relative positions of concrete members (b) size of members (c) thickness of slabs (d) permissible loads in relation to casting times.					M1 Except where otherwise stated, formwork is measured to concrete surfaces of the finished structure which require temporary support during casting	D1 Plain formwork surfaces are those which contain no steps, rebates, pockets or other discontinuities D2 Formwork left in is that which is not designed to remain in position but is nonetheless impossible to remove D3 Permanent formwork is that which is designed to remain in position	C1 Formwork is deemed to include adaptation to accommodate projecting pipes, reinforcing bars and the like C2 Formwork is deemed to include all cutting, splayed edges and the like	S1 Materials and propping requirements for permanent formwork S2 Basic finish where not at the discretion of the Contractor
CLASSIFICATION TABLE								
1 Sides of foundations 2 Sides of ground beams and edges of beds 3 Edges of suspended slabs 4 Sides of upstands 5 Steps in top surfaces 6 Steps in soffits 7 Machine bases and plinths	1 Plain vertical 2 Dimensioned description	1 Height ≤ 250 mm 2 Height 250 - 500 mm 3 Height 500 mm - 1.00 m	m	1 Left in 2 Permanent 3 Curved, radii stated	M2 Passings of ground beams are not deducted from area of formwork	D4 Foundations include bases and pile caps D5 Edges of suspended slabs exclude those associated with attached beams at slab perimeters		
		4 Height > 1.00 m	m^2					
8 Soffits of slabs 9 Soffits of landings (nr)	1 Slab thickness ≤ 200 mm 2 and thereafter in 100 mm stages	1 Horizontal 2 Sloping ≤ 15° 3 Sloping > 15°	m^2	1 Left in 2 Permanent 3 Curved, radii stated 4 Height to soffit ≤ 1.50 m 5 and thereafter in 1.50 m stages	M3 Voids ≤ 5.00 m^2 irrespective of location are not deducted from the area measured M4 Soffits of coffered or troughed slabs are measured as if to a plain surface M5 The thickness of the coffered or troughed slabs stated is measured overall	D6 Formwork to soffits of slabs includes formwork to landings occurring at floor levels D7 Soffits of coffered or troughed slabs include margins which are ≤ 500 mm wide		
10 Soffits of coffered or troughed slabs	1 Size of mould and profile, centres of mould, and slab thickness stated		m^2					
11 Top formwork			m^2	1 Left in 2 Permanent 3 Curved, radii stated	M6 Top formwork is measured for surfaces sloping > 15° and where otherwise specifically required			
12 Walls		1 Vertical 2 Battered	m^2	1 Left in 2 Permanent to both sides 3 Curved, radii stated	M7 Voids ≤ 5.00 m^2 irrespective of location are not deducted from the area measured for walls	D8 Walls include isolated columns and column casings whose length on plan is > four times their		

applies only to those parts of the work for which drawings are not available.

For convenience, the SMM7 requirements for provision of drawings with bills of quantities are given in an appendix to the Production Drawings Code.

Provision of specification

The tabulated rules for each work section contain, in addition to the rules for measurement, requirements for the provision of specification information. They are usually stated in general terms, e.g. 'Details of materials', 'Method of fixing', but in all cases the requirements are subject to the SMM7 General Rule to the effect that *'more detailed information than is required by these rules shall be given where necessary in order to define the precise nature and extent of the required work'.*

Clearly, it is impracticable to include full specification in the quantities, and the SMM7 General Rules provide that descriptive information *'may be given in documents (e.g. drawings and specification) separate from the bills of quantities if a precise and unique cross reference is given in its place in the description of the item concerned'.* Thus SMM7 is linked to the Project Specification Code (see page 20), which recommends that full specification is normally given only in the project specification, the drawings and quantities identifying the various kinds and qualities of work by a few carefully chosen words with, as appropriate, a reference to the relevant clause(s) in the specification (see Figures P and Q). The use of CAWS for arrangement of both specifications and quantities is fundamental to this co-ordination of descriptive information.

Whilst SMM7 requires the provision of adequate specification, it does not define this in detail. The test is that the designers' requirements are met and that there will be no contractor's claims based on inadequate specification. The specification checklists included in Part B of the Project Specification Code will help practitioners ensure that relevant specification information is not overlooked.

Preliminaries

SMM7 introduces significant changes in the rules for Preliminaries. Employer's requirements and limitations are now to be clearly separated from the contractor's general cost items for management, staff, accommodation, facilities, plant and temporary works. Provision is made for the inclusion of costs of both fixed and time related items – thus contractors will be encouraged to price in a way which reflects the costs arising from establishing their organisation on site, running it, then removing it on completion of the work.

Phraseologies for bills

In recent years, quantity surveyors have made wide use of 'phrase libraries' or 'phraseologies', i.e. documents from which terms can be drawn in a systematic way to build up the bill item descriptions. SMM7 has been designed so that it can be used as a basic phraseology, as shown in Figure P. However the new format for the rules does not inhibit the use of traditional prose in the writing of bills of quantities if so desired.

'SMM7 Standard Descriptions', a commercially available co-ordinated phraseology, is being prepared by the Property Services Agency with the support of the RICS and BEC. It will expand the basic SMM7 terminology into structured staccato phrases and is being designed for computer use. Publication is expected early in 1988.

Code for Bills of Quantities

This is a companion document to SMM7 including supplementary and explanatory material which does not have the same contractual status as the SMM7 rules.

13 Beams (nr) 14 Beam casings (nr) 15 Columns (nr) 16 Column casings (nr)	1 Attached to slabs 2 Attached to walls 3 Isolated	1 Regular shaped, shape stated	m²	1 Left in 2 Permanent 3 Curved, radii stated 4 Height to soffit ≤ 1.50 m 5 and thereafter in 1.50 m stages	M10 Passings of subsidiary beams or other projections are not deducted from areas of formwork but such intersections are dee[illegible] constitute the comme[illegible] ad[illegible]	D9 Where a downstand beam is formed by temporary formwork but the slab is supported by permanent formwork th[illegible] downstand bea[illegible] regarded [illegible] be[illegible]	C3 Formwork to beams, columns and casings is deemed to include ends	
		2 Irregular shaped, dimensioned diagram	m					
17 Recesses (nr) 18 Nibs (nr) 19 Rebates (nr)	1 Plain rectangular, size stated 2 Dimensioned diagram		m	1 Extra over the formwork in which they occur 2 Left in 3 Permanent 4 Curved, radii stated	M13 The extra over superficially measured formwork in which recesses, nibs or rebates occur is stated		C4 Formwork to recesses is deemed to include ends	
20 Extra over a basic finish for formed finishes	1 Slabs 2 Walls 3 Beams 4 Columns 5 Others, stated		m²			D11 Formed finishes are those where a finish other than a basic finish is required		S3 Details of formed finishes

Figure P
Use of SMM7 as a basic phraseology, including cross-reference to the specification (see Figure Q)

	E20 FORMWORK FOR IN SITU CONCRETE (continued) E20				
	Formwork; basic finish E20/710				
	Soffits of slabs				
A	not exceeding 200 mm; thick; horizontal; propping height 3.00-4.50 m	186 m²			
	Beams attached to slabs				
B	plain rectangular; 300 x 450 mm; height to soffit 3.0-4.5 m (8 nr)	27 m²			
	Extra over basic finish for plain smooth finish E20/720				
C	slabs	162 m²			
D	beams	22 m²			

Figure Q

E20 FORMWORK FOR IN SITU CONCRETE (continued) E20

FORMED FINISHES

710 BASIC FINISH: no particular requirements, except those for tolerances and full compaction.

720 PLAIN SMOOTH FINISH:
1. Produce an even finish with a sheet material (e.g. plywood), with panels arranged in a regular pattern as a feature of the surface.
2. Abrupt irregularities to be not greater than 5 mm. Gradual irregularities, expressed as maximum permissible deviation from a 1 m straight edge, to be not greater than 5 mm.
3. Variation in colour resulting from the use of an impermeable form lining will be permitted but the surface to be free from discolouration due to contamination or grout leakage.
4. Blowholes less than 10 mm in diameter will be permitted but otherwise surface to be free from voids, honeycombing, segregation and other large defects.
5. Projecting fins are to be removed and rubbed down with a carborundum stone but otherwise the finish is to be left as struck. Making good of small defects will normally be permitted after inspection by SO.
6. Arrisses to be chamfered with a 12 mm corner face.
7. Formwork tie holes to be in an approved regular pattern, filled with matching mortar to an approved sample.

Complete a sample area of the finished work, size 10 m², in advance of the remainder, in an approved location, and obtain approval of appearance before proceeding.

Example project documents

Student residences
St Aidan's College
University of Durham

Architect:
FaulknerBrowns

Services Engineer:
Cairns and Byles

Structural Engineer:
Cundall Johnstone and Partners

Quantity Surveyor:
Gleeds

Contractor:
Shepherd Construction Ltd

The project

The example project is an extension to a residential college comprising 42 study bedrooms, laundry and cooking facilities and one tutor's flat. It was constructed in 1981–2 and the contract value was approximately £350,000.

It was chosen as the example for this Guide because:

- Without being too large it is clearly a with quantities project.
- Despite its size it is simple, and therefore reasonably relevant as a 'small jobs' example.
- A full design team was employed.
- The drawings were comprehensive, and structured to follow the recommendations of the Building Research Establishment.
- A comprehensive specification had been prepared.

The drawings

The structure and content of the Architect's, Structural Engineer's and Services Engineer's drawings have been reviewed against the Production Drawings Code and adjusted to some extent. A complete list of drawings is given on page 32 in order that the overall structure can be appreciated.

Selected drawings have been re-drafted to comply with the Code and are shown on pages 33 to 45. No attempt has been made to produce specially high standards of draughtsmanship or lettering, indeed part of the implied message is to avoid unnecessary work in order to leave sufficient time for the provision of all the information which is needed.

The drawings are included merely as illustrations of co-ordinated project information. They are not put forward as models of design or construction technology and therefore should not be criticised as such. The construction of the project complied with the Building Regulations current at the time but does not necessarily comply with the present Regulations.

The specification

The original specification was based on NBS, British Standards and proprietary information as current in 1981. Selected sections have been re-drafted to comply with the Project Specification Code and are shown on pages 48 to 51. British Standard references have been updated, but the references to proprietary products have not been changed and may no longer be current. The proprietary names are those specified in the actual project – they are included simply to make the examples realistic and recommendation of the products is not implied.

As part of the CPI initiative NBS will be re-published in 1988 to comply with CAWS and the Project Specification Code. The selected example sections have been based on drafts for the forthcoming new edition of NBS (kindly provided by NBS Ltd).

In order to show three sections of the specification within the available space, an unusual presentation has been adopted. For each section, a complete list of clause 'keyword' headings is given. Alongside, the full text of selected clauses is given so that at least some of the cross-references given on the drawings and in the quantities can be followed through.

The quantities

Selected sections have been re-drafted to comply with SMM7 and are shown on pages 52 to 54. As with the original quantities, extensive references to the specification are given.

The overall arrangement of the specification and quantities is shown on pages 46 and 47. For such a simple project the production of separate bills for Substructure, Superstructure and External Works was considered unnecessary.

Several types of bill summary are possible with CAWS and two examples are shown on page 55. In the first example monetary collections are provided at the end of each group of work sections (e.g. F Masonry) the totals of which are then transferred to the General Summary which in this case contains 18 items.

In the second example collections are provided at the end of each work section (e.g. F10 Brick/Block walling) the totals of which are transferred to the General Summary. This arrangement gives a separate total for every separate type of work, but results in a long General Summary – in the case of the student residences project 54 items running to two pages.

Example production drawings

Key To Drawing Numbering

First digit: source of drawings
A = Architect
S = Structural Engineer
M = Mechanical Engineer
E = Electrical Engineer

Second digit: information type
L = Location drawing
A = Assembly drawing
C = Component drawing

Third digit: element group
(0) = General
(1) = Substructure
(2) = Superstructure
(3) = Openings, etc.
(4) = Finishes
(5) = Piped & ducted services
(6) = Electrical services
(7) = Fixtures & fittings
(9) = External works

Schedule of Drawings

The drawings are listed in Information type – Element group – Source sequence. They could, alternatively, have been listed in Source – Information type – Element group sequence.

Location drawings (A1 size)

AL(0)1	Site plan, Access, Setting out	1:200
AL(0)2	Overall key plans	1:100
AL(0)3	House + Flat floor plans	1:50
AL(0)4	House + Flat roof plan	1:50
AL(0)5	House + Flat, E + W elevations	1:50
AL(0)6	N + S elevations, House section	1:50
SL(1)1–6	Foundations	1:50 & 1:20
AL(2)1	Blockwork setting out	1:50
AL(2)2	Holes through first floor slab	1:50
SL(2)1	First floor concrete slab	1:50 & 1:20
SL(2)2	Roof	1:50 & 1:20
AL(3)1	External openings schedule	–
AL(3)2	Internal openings schedule	–
AL(4)1	Finishes schedule	–
AL(5)1	Drainage + service entries	1:100 & 1:50
AL(5)3	Manhole + cover schedule	–
AL(5)4	Above ground drainage	1:50
ML(5)1	Site plan: gas + water	1:500
ML(5)2	Heating + water + gas, house units	1:50
ML(5)3	Heating + water + gas, house units	1:50
ML(5)4	Heating + water + gas, flat unit	1:50
EL(6)1	Site plan: main cable route	1:500
EL(6)2	Electrical wiring	1:50
EL(6)3	Schematic wiring diagrams	NTS
AL(9)1	Landscape + drainage	1:200

Assembly drawings (A1 size)

AA(1)1–5	Ground slab junction details	1:10
AA(2)01–14	External wall details: plans	1:5
AA(2)15–19	External wall details (W): sections	1:5
AA(2)20–23	External wall details (E): sections	1:5
AA(2)30–35	Zinc cladding details	1:2
AA(2)36–44	Zinc cladding details	1:2
AA(2)46–50	Zinc cladding isometrics	1:5
AA(2)60–69	Internal wall details: sections	1:5
AA(2)70–80	Internal wall details: plans	1:5
AA(2)81–89	Roof to Tutor's Flat stair	1:20 & 1:5
AA(2)91–95	Roof details	1:5
SA(2)1–4	Reinforcement details	1:10
SA(2)1–3	Roof details	1:10
AA(3)1–5	External opening details	1:5
AA(3)6–19	Internal opening details	1:5
MA(5)1	Heating control panels	FS
MA(5)2	Boiler details	1:10
MA(5)3	Bathroom + toilet extract ventilation	NTS
MA(5)4	Laundry water supply + ventilation	1:20
MA(5)5	Towel rail + stair radiator details	1:20
MA(5)6	Fire hydrant chamber	1:10
AA(7)1–7	Fittings to student rooms	1:10
AA(7)8–13	Fittings to pantries + kitchen + laundry	1:10
AA(9)1–4	External works details	1:10

Component drawings (A1 size)

AC(2)1	Trussed rafters	1:10
AC(3)1	Timber windows	1:10 & 1:2
AC(3)2	External doors	1:10 & 1:2
AC(3)3	Glazed screen to pantry	1:10 & 1:2
AC(7)1	Desk worktops	1:10 & 1:2

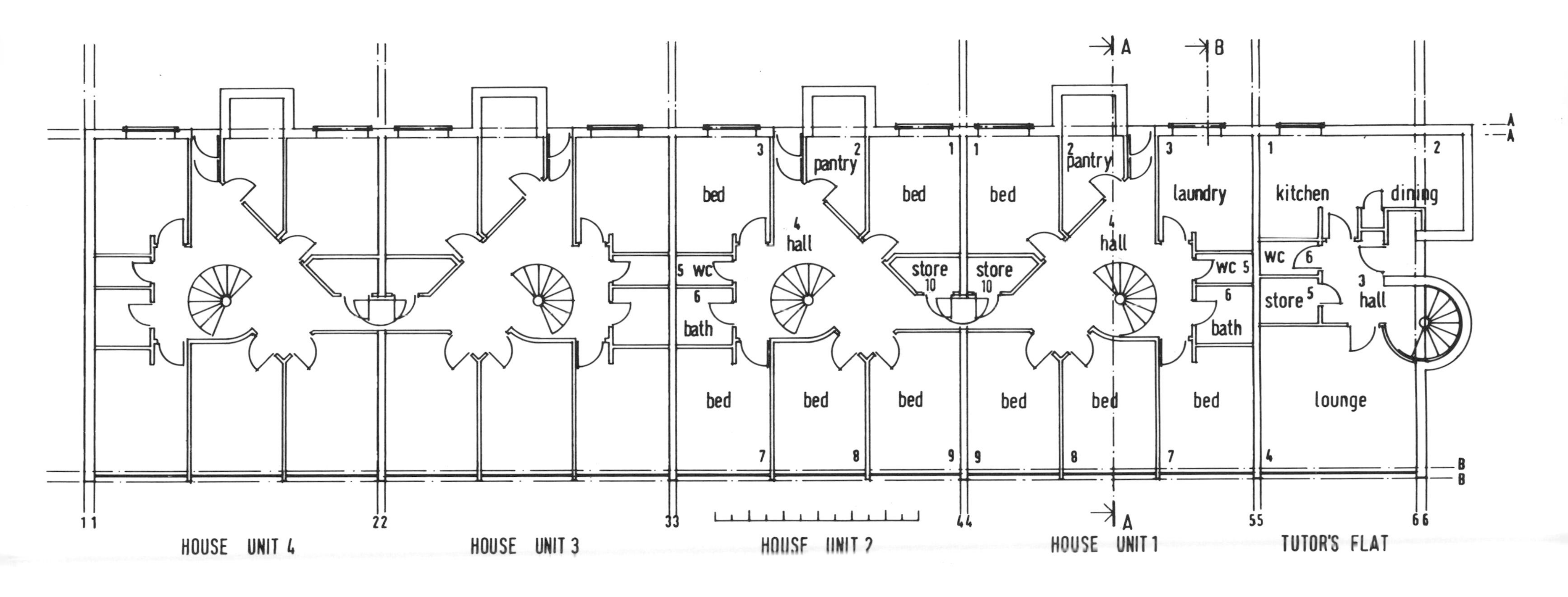

This is a general 'context' drawing, showing the overall size of the building and pattern of repetition. It was quickly produced from a design drawing base negative. The drawing includes both ground and first floors at 1:100 scale; the ground floor only is reproduced here.

AL(O)2 Overall key plans

AA(2)10
W1
W2
AA(2)13
W1 AC(3)1-2
A
A
AA(2)9
W2
11
12
13
7
8
D21
D12
AA(2)75
D10
D11
AA(2)74
D20
AA(2)71
AA(2)70
AA(2)76
AA(2)78
20
AA(2)70
14
15
D13
D9
11
AA(2)77
D8
AA(2)79
D18
AA(2)74
D19
16
D14
9
AA(2)74
AA(2)73
D7
AA(2)72
AA(2)75
D17
D16
D15
Fitted furniture
AA(7)2
19
18
17
10
Desk worktop
AA(7)1
AA(2)14
AA(2)12
AA(2)11
C
C
44
55
66

HOUSE UNIT 1

TUTOR'S FLAT
First floor

This is part of drawing AL(0)3 – see below

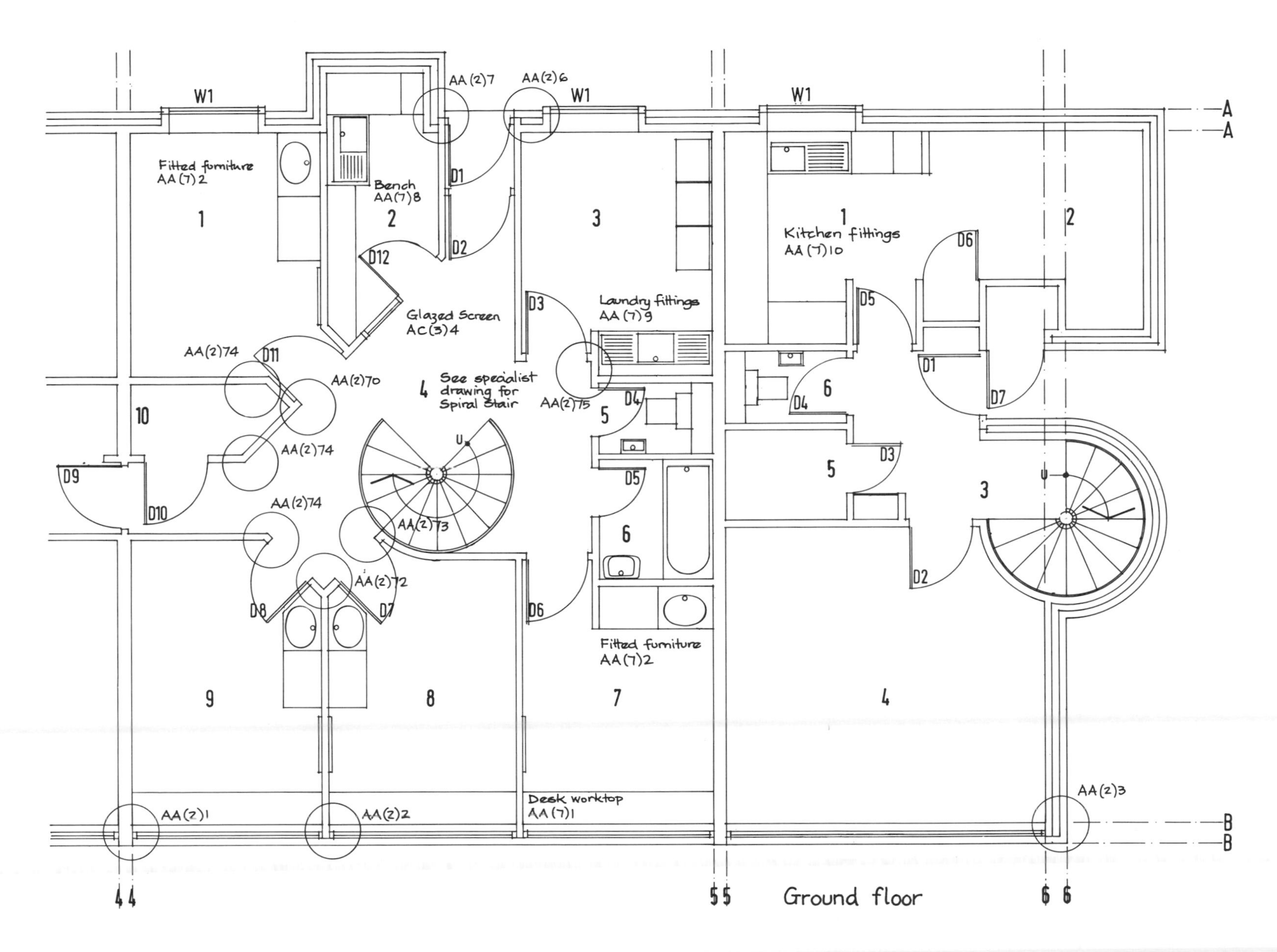

The 1:50 General Arrangement drawings AL(0)3/4/5/6 give a general appreciation of the building and act as a key to more detailed information given on Assembly drawings – see page 44. For the sake of clarity they do not give detailed specification references – these are given on more specific drawings, particularly Assembly drawings.

AL (O) 3 House + Flat floor plans

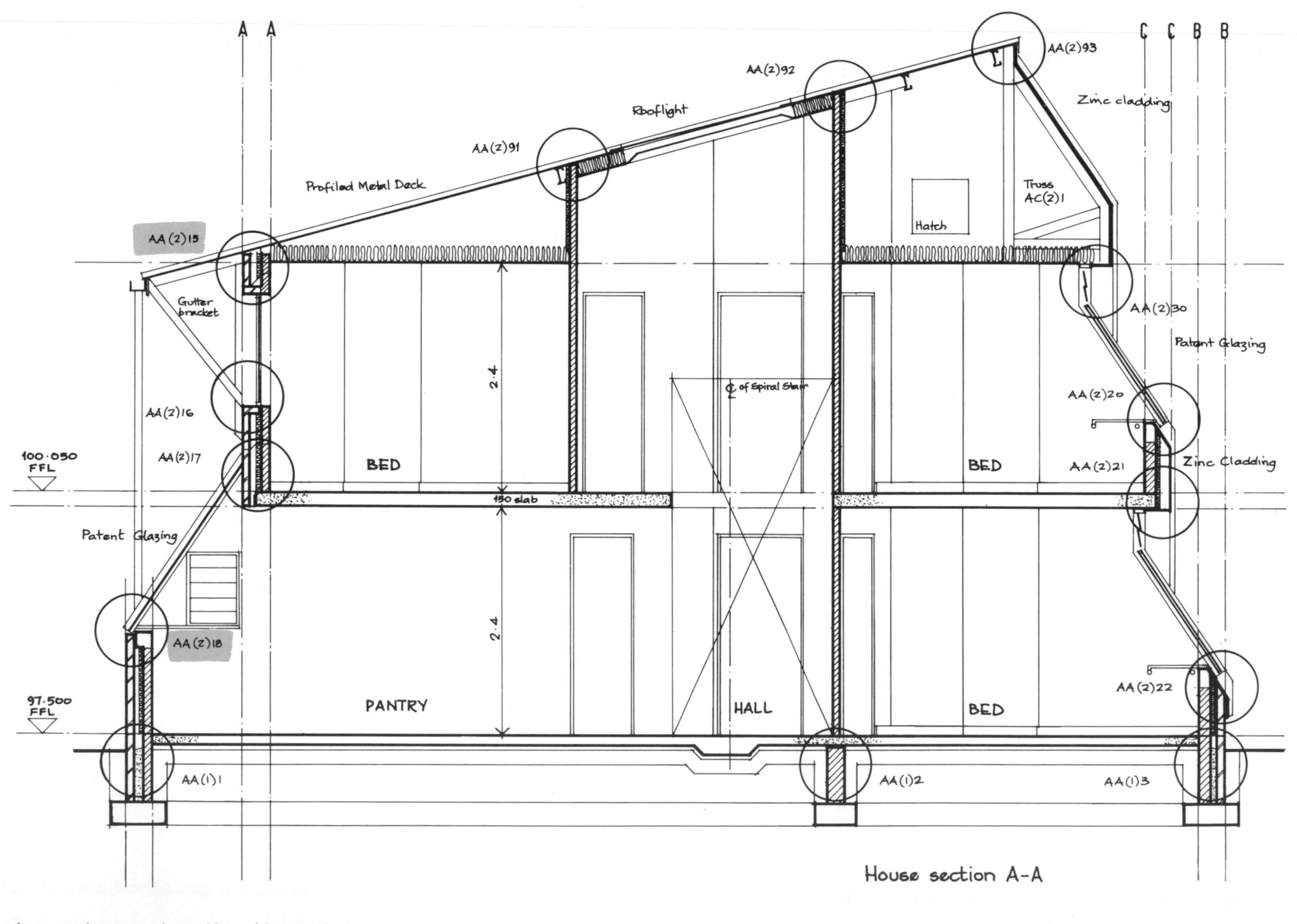

This drawing (part only reproduced here) is another from the General Arrangement set – see notes on page 35. 1/50 scale was chosen in order to avoid the temptation to give too much detail, which would have merely repeated information better given on the Assembly drawings.

AL(0)6 N + S elevations, House section

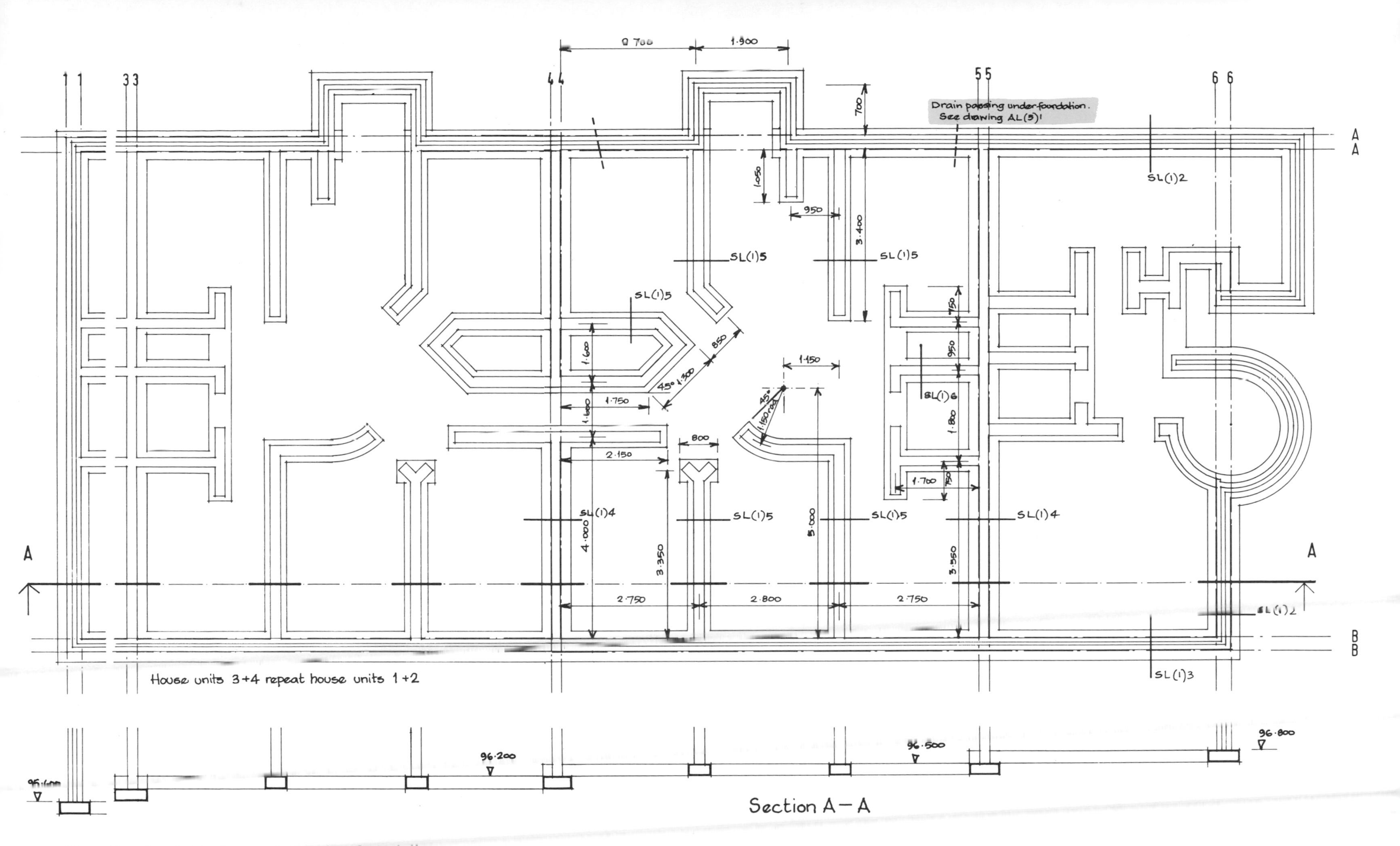

The Structural Engineer drew the foundations rather than the Architect. Because the foundation plan occupied only a part of the A1 sheet, the 1:20 details were also included.

SL(1)1-6 Foundations

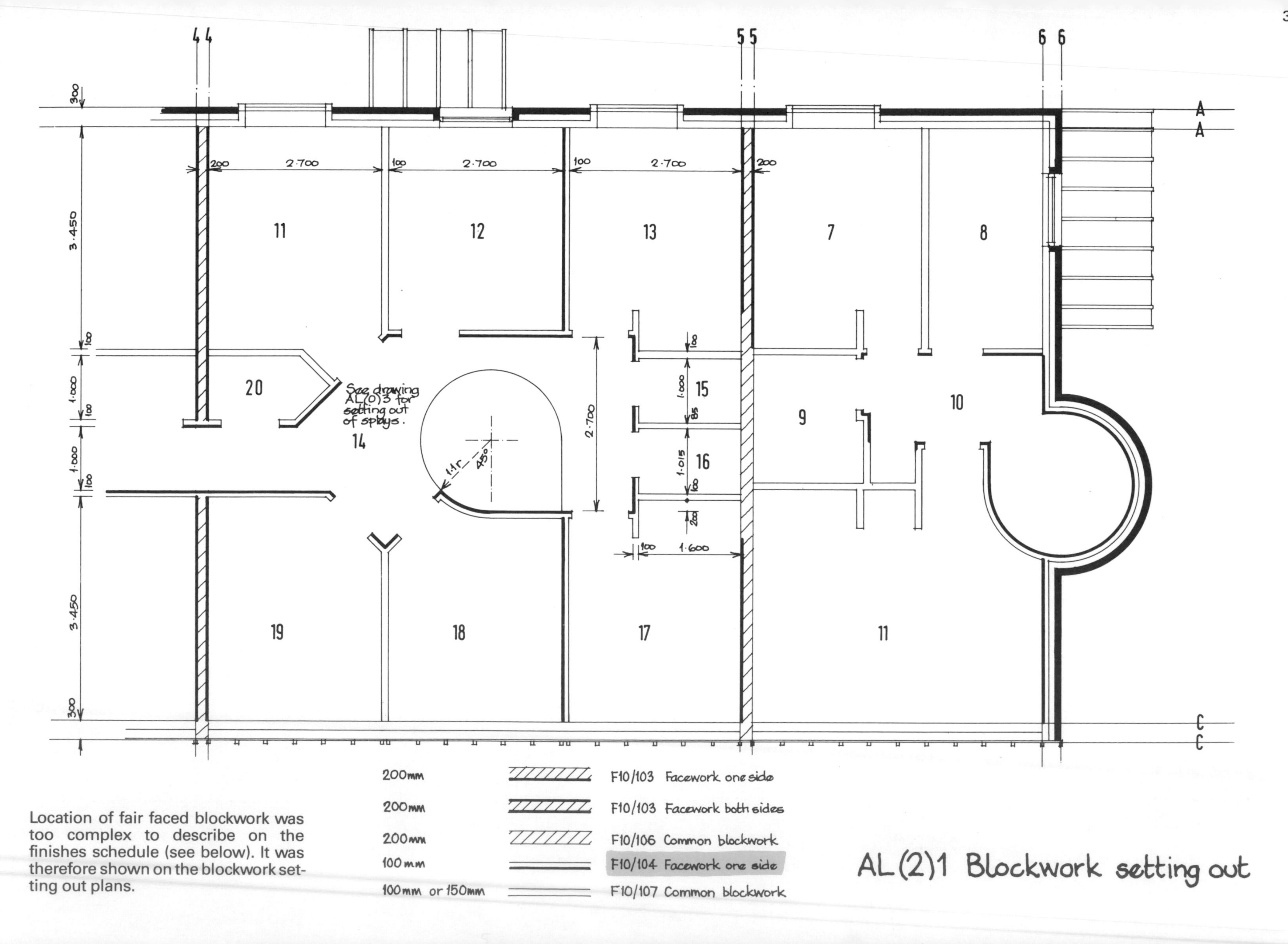

AL(2)1 Blockwork setting out

Location of fair faced blockwork was too complex to describe on the finishes schedule (see below). It was therefore shown on the blockwork setting out plans.

GROUND FLOOR	SPECIFICATION REFERENCES	H1 BED	H2 PANTRY	H3 LAUNDRY	H4 HALL	H5 WC.	H6 BATH	H7 BED
WALLS	Fair faced blockwork as dwg. AL(2)1, not painted Other walls either: – Ceramic tiles on render M40/101 or – Plaster M20/101, painted Emulsion paint M60/101 (08 B 15) Eggshell paint M60/102 (08 B 15)	Emulsion	Emulsion	Eggshell	F.F. block not painted	Ceramic tile	Ceramic tile	Emulsion
CEILINGS	Plasterboard K10 Eggshell paint M60/102 (white) Textured paint M60/103 (white)	Textured paint to concrete	Textured paint to concrete	Textured paint to concrete	Textured paint to concrete	Eggshell on plasterboard	Eggshell on plasterboard	Textured paint to concrete
FLOORS	Power floated concrete to receive: – Carpet (by client) – Vinyl tiles M50 – Quarry tiles M40/102	Carpet	Vinyl tiles	Quarry tiles	Quarry tiles	Quarry tiles	Quarry tiles	Carpet
SKIRTINGS	Vinyl tile M50/101 Quarry tile M40/102 Softwood P20 Preservative stain M60/110 (black)	Softwood stained	Vinyl tile	Quarry tile	Softwood stained	Quarry tile	Quarry tile	Softwood stained
DOORS/GLAZED SCREENS	Preservative stain M60/110 (black) Wood primer and gloss paint M60/108 (04 E 53)	Frame stained Door gloss	Frame stained Door gloss	Frame stained Door gloss	Frame stained Door gloss	Frame stained Door gloss	Frame stained Door gloss	Frame stained Door gloss
WINDOWS	Preservative stain M60/110 (black) Calcium plumbate primer and gloss M60/107 (white)	Stained + CP and gloss		Stained + CP and gloss				Stained + CP and
RADIATORS & PIPES	Zinc primer and gloss paint M60/105 Patch zinc primer and gloss paint M60/106 (white)	Pipes ZP+gloss Radiator – patch ZP+gloss	Pipes ZP+gloss Radiator – patch ZP+gloss	Pipes ZP+gloss Radiator – patch ZP+gloss		Pipes ZP+gloss	Pipes ZP+gloss	
PINBOARDS	Pinboard N10/340 Flame retardant paint M60/109	1200 x 900 FR paint						
FURNITURE/ FEATURES	Clear coating M60/111 Calcium plumbate + gloss M60/107 10 B 53	Wardrobe + vanitory unit AA(7)1–7 Clear coating	Sink unit + kitchen units AA(7) 8–13	Sink unit AA(7) 8–13	Spiral stair L31 CP + gloss			

FIRST FLOOR	SPECIFICATION REFERENCES	H11 BED	H12 BED	H13 BED	H14 H'
WALLS	Fair faced blockwork as dwg AL(2)1, not painted Other walls either: – Ceramic tiles on render M40/101 or – Plaster M20/101, painted Emulsion paint M60/101 (08 B 15) Eggshell paint M60/102 (08 B 15)	Emulsion	Emulsion	Emulsion	
CEILINGS	Plasterboard K10 Eggshell paint M60/102 (white) Textured paint M60/103 (white)	Textured paint to plasterboard	Textured p' to plas'		
FLOORS	Power floated concrete to receive: – Carpet (by client) – Vinyl tiles M50 – Quarry tiles M40/102	Carpet			

AL(4)1 Finishes schedule

The column for 'Specification references' was introduced so that the descriptions given elsewhere could be abbreviated. Fixed furniture and features were included in the schedule so that the finishes thereto could be given.

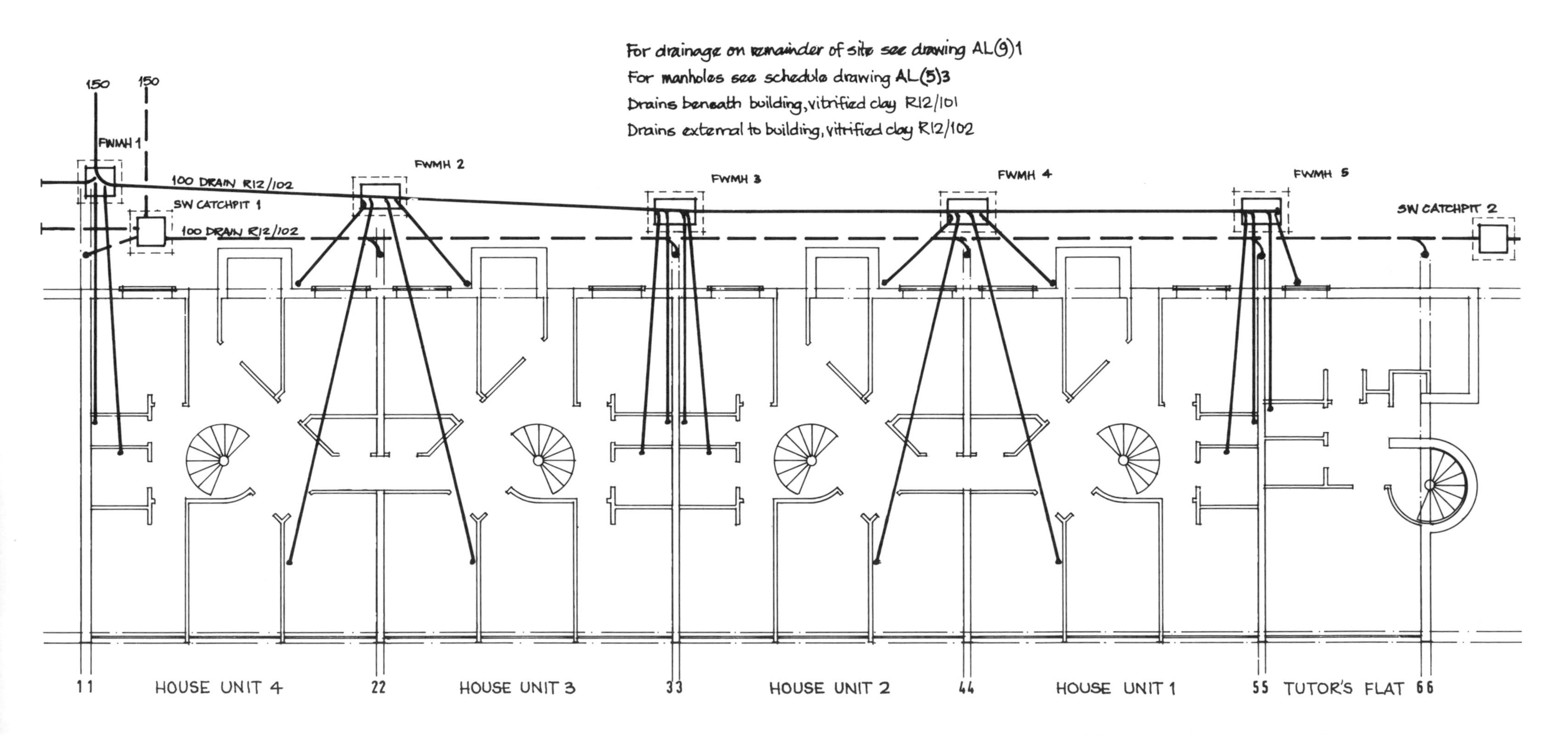

This is part of drawing AL(5) 1 – see below

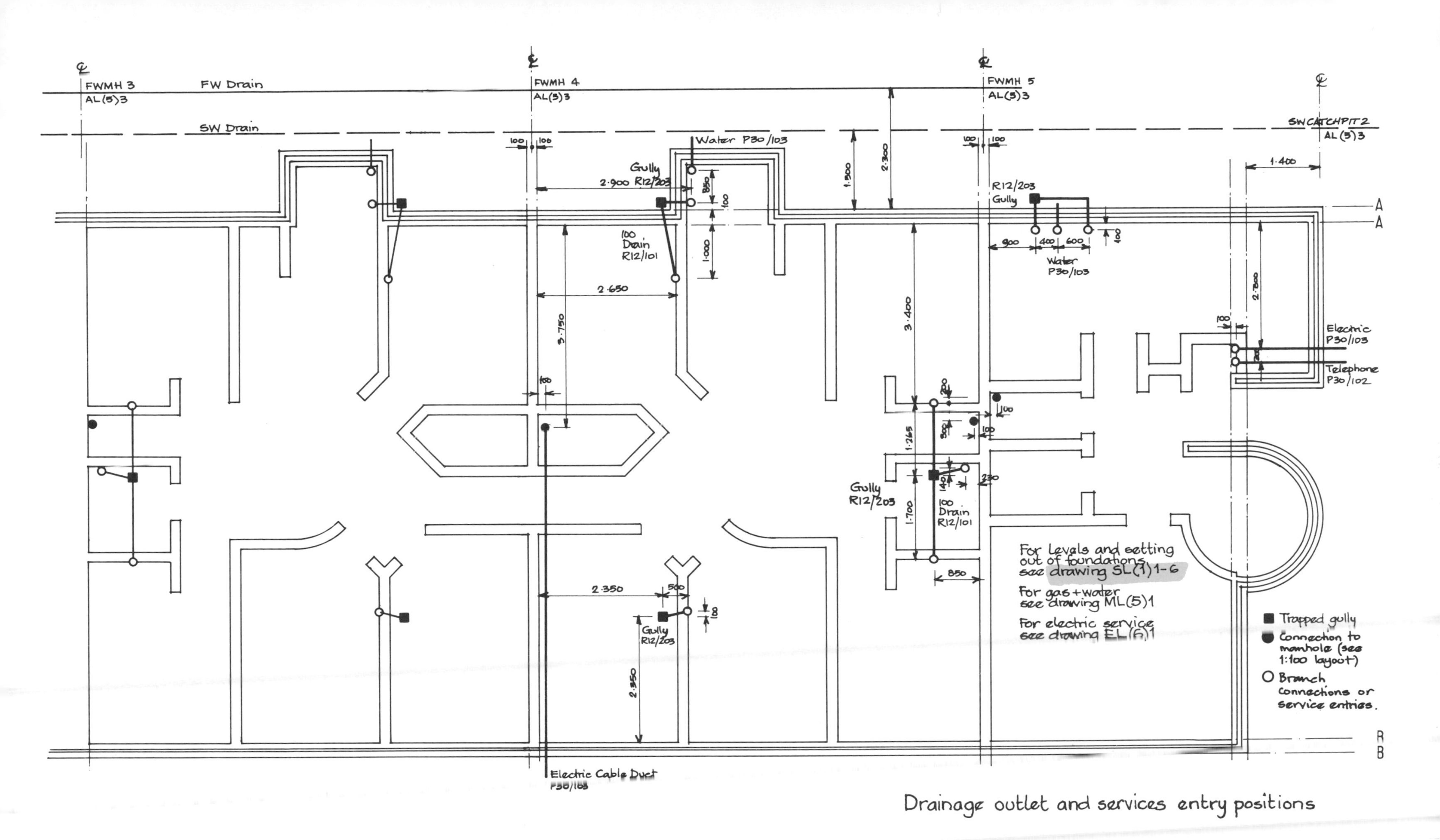

The underground services layout and service entry/exit positions were too complex to show clearly on one plan. They were therefore separated but shown on the same sheet. Note the references given to related foundation and site services drawings.

AL(5)1 Drainage + service entries

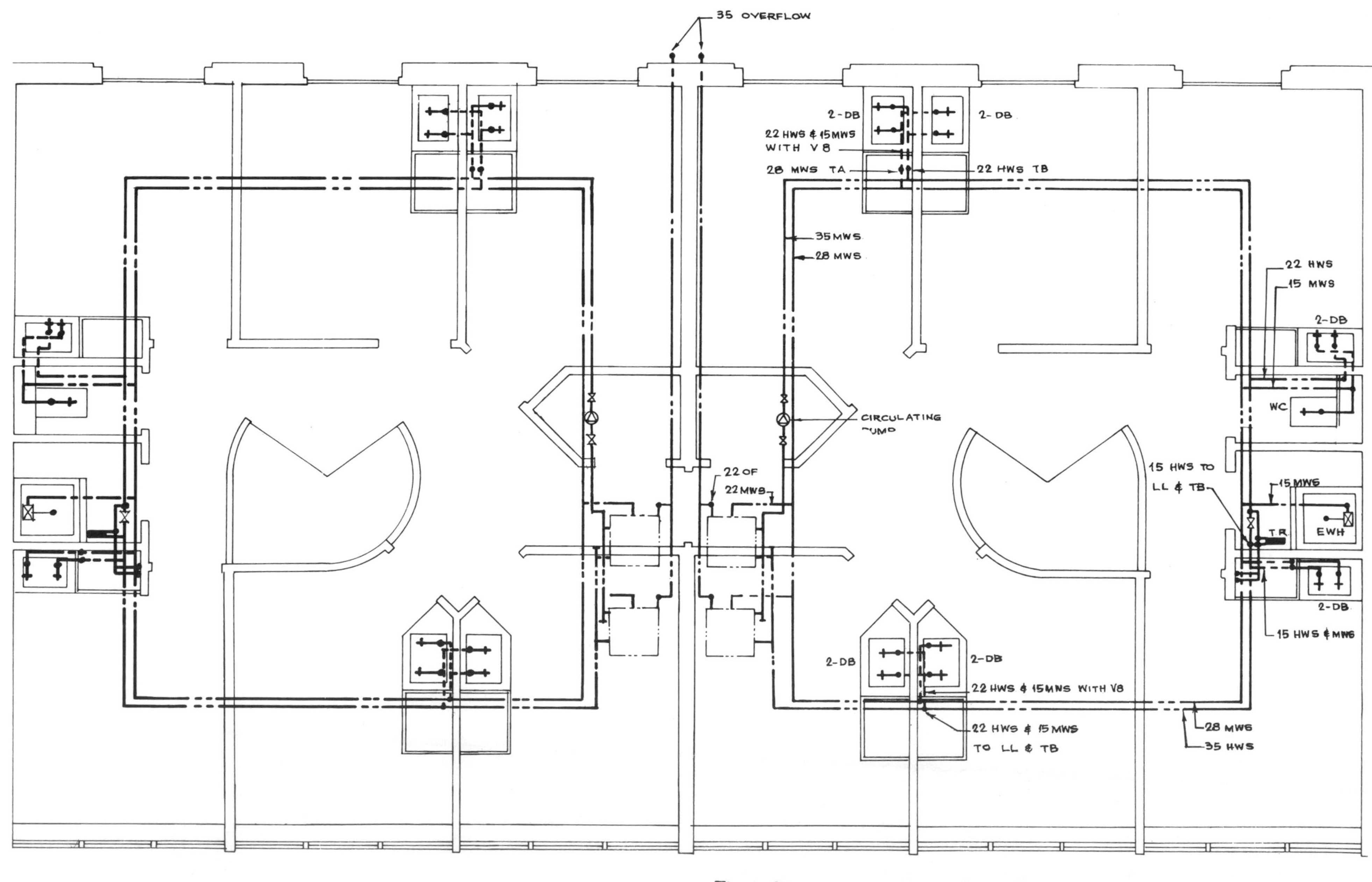

First floor, hot + cold water : See specification section S12

This is part of drawing ML(5)3 – see below

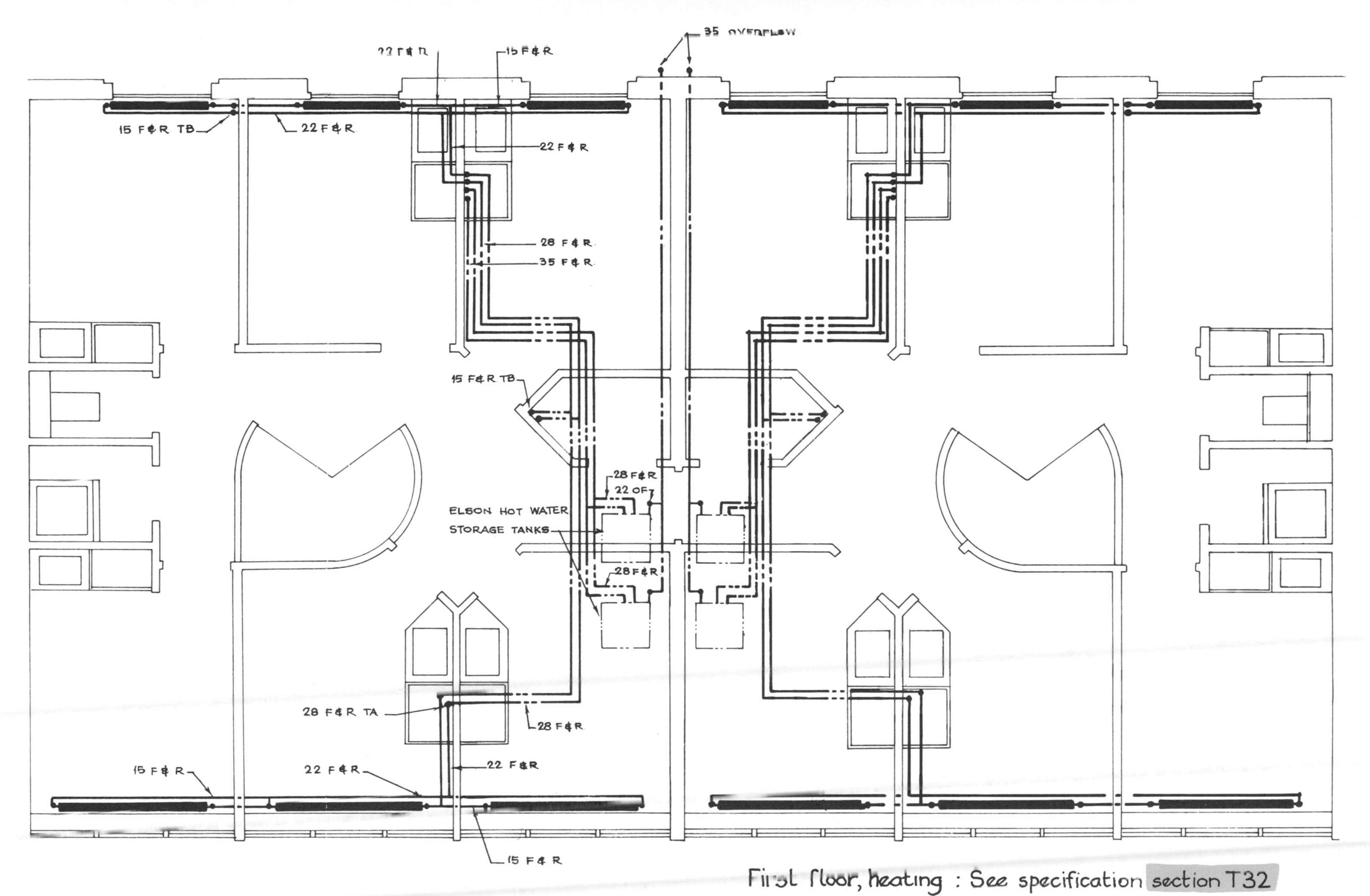

First floor, heating : See specification section T32

The LTHW heating and H + C water installations were too congested to be superimposed. They were therefore separated but shown on the same sheet.

ML(5)3 First floor; Heating +hot and cold water

40mm Profiled Metal deck H31/101
Course of snap headers
M.S. Purlin
30mm insulation F30/560
Cavity tray F30/030
Perpend units F30/540
Mesh strip reinforcement F30/450
Dpc F30/030
15mm insulation F30/570
Facings both inside and outside F10/101
Metal window L11
175mm insulation F30/560
75x75sw wallplate top edge splayed at 15° bolted to m.s. angle.
38x50sw wall trim
Plasterboard and skim ceiling M20/102
100mm blockwork F10/107
Two coat plaster M20/101

AA(2)15 Circular window head/roof junction

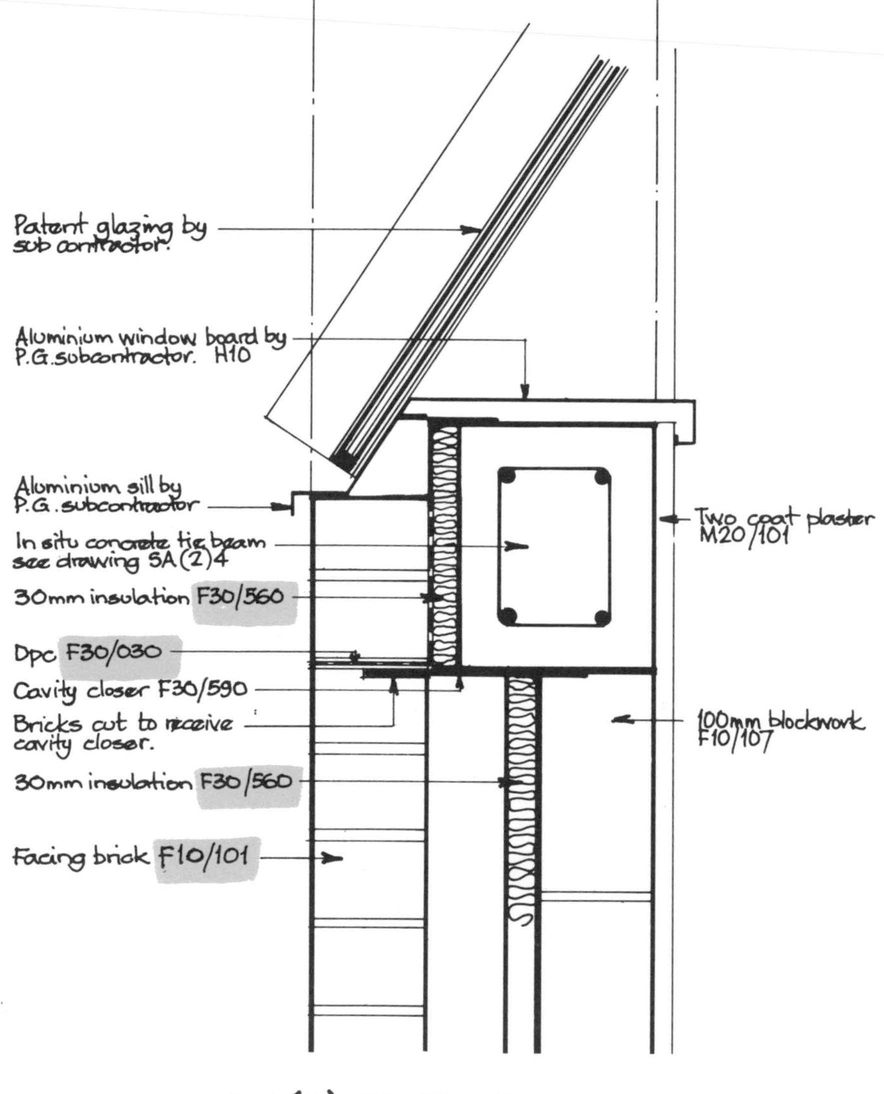

AA(2)18 Pantry glazing-sill

The Location drawings refer specifically to particular Assembly details, which therefore need to be separately numbered. Several details are shown on each Assembly drawing, the number of that drawing comprising the numbers of the details included on it, e.g. AA(2) 15–19. As explained on page 35, specification references are given on the more specific drawings, particularly Assembly drawings.

AA(2)15-19 External wall details (W): Sections

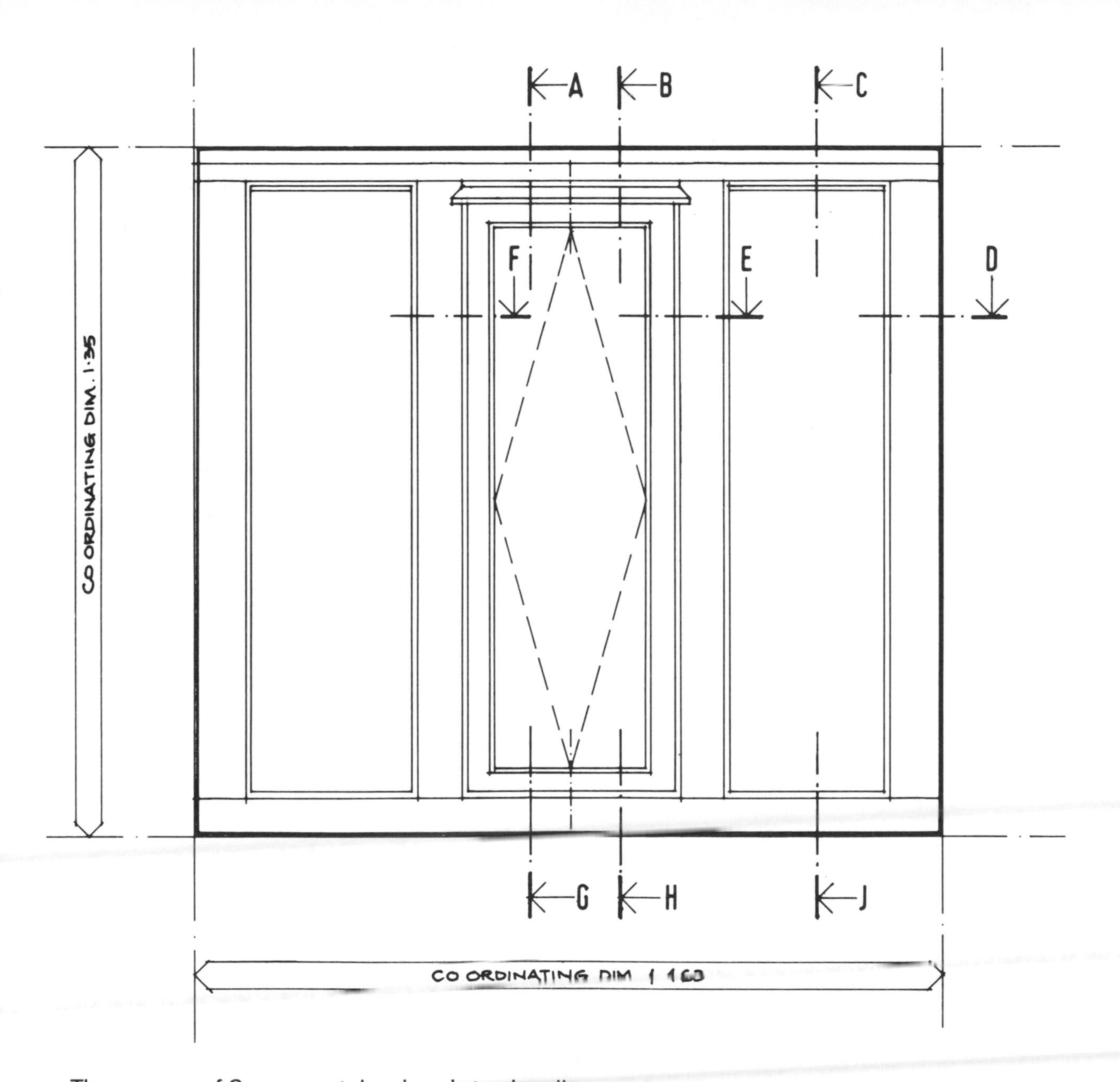

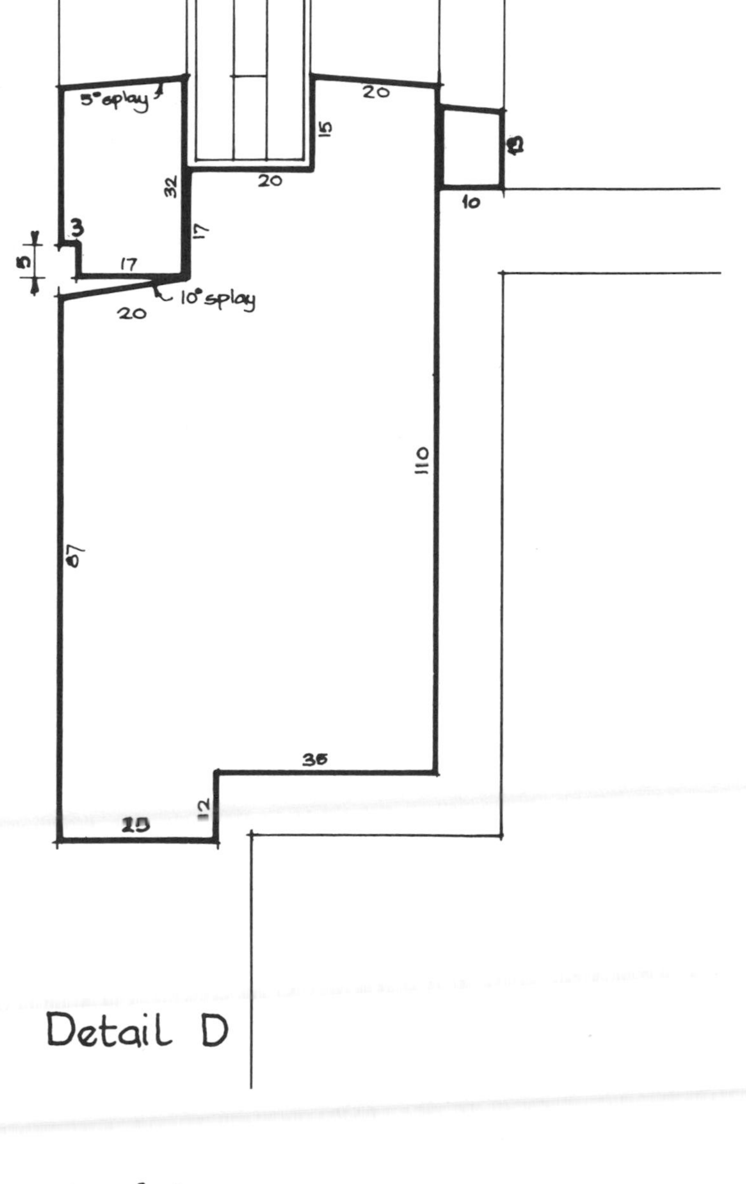

The purpose of Component drawings is to give all information necessary for the manufacture of the component. This drawing includes details A, B, C, D, E, F, G, H and J as shown on the key elevation.

AC (3) 1 Timber Windows

Arrangement of specification and quantities

				BILL NUMBER 1 SPECIFICATION		BILL NUMBER 2: QUANTITIES	
A	PRELIMINARIES/ GENERAL CONDITIONS (INCLUDING DAYWORKS, PC AND PROVISION SUMS)	A1	The project generally	A1	1	A1	1
		A2	The Contract	A2	4	A2	2
		A3	Employer's requirements	A3	7	A3	3
		A4	Contractor's general cost items	A4	-	A4	4
		A5	Work by others or subject to instruction	A5	17	A5	6
D	GROUNDWORK	D20	Excavating and filling	D20	18	D20	10
E	IN SITU CONCRETE/ LARGE PRECAST CONCRETE	E10	In situ concrete	E10	20	E10	12
		E20	Formwork for in situ concrete	E20	28	E20	15
		E30	Reinforcement for in situ concrete	E30	30	E30	17
		E40	Designed joints in in situ concrete	E40	31	E40	18
		E41	Worked finishes to in situ concrete	E41	32	E41	18
		E60	Precast concrete decking	E60	34	E60	19
F	MASONRY	F10	Brick/Block walling	F10	36	F10	20
		F30	Accessories/Sundry items for brick/ block walling	F30	40	F30	23
G	STRUCTURAL/CARCASSING METAL/TIMBER	G10	Structural steel framing	G10	44	G10	26
		G20	Carpentry/First fixing	G20	45	G20	27
H	CLADDING/COVERING	H10	Patent glazing	H10	50	H10	33
		H31	Metal profiled sheet covering	H31	52	H31	35
		H71	Lead sheet flashings	H71	54	H71	37
		H74	Zinc sheet coverings/flashings	H74	55	H74	38
J	WATERPROOFING	J40	Flexible sheet damp proof membranes	J40	58	J40	41
K	LININGS	K10	Plasterboard dry lining	K10	59	K10	42
		K11	Rigid sheet flooring/sheathing	K11	60	K11	43
L	WINDOWS/DOORS STAIRS	L10	Timber windows	L10	61	L10	45
		L11	Metal windows	L11	62	L11	45
		L12	Plastics rooflights	L12	63	L12	45
		L20	Timber doors/screens/hatches	L20	65	L20	46
		L31	Metal stairs/balustrades	L31	67	L31	49
		L40	General glazing	L40	68	L40	50

M	SURFACE FINISHES	M20	Plastered/Rendered coatings	M20	71	M20	52
		M40	Quarry/Ceramic tiling	M40	74	M40	54
		M50	Plastics tiling	M50	76	M50	56
		M60	Painting/Clear finishing	M60	77	M60	57
N	FURNITURE/EQUIPMENT	N10	General fixtures/furnishings	N10	83	N10	61
		N11	Domestic kitchen fittings	N11	-	N11	62
		N13	Sanitary appliances	N13	-	N13	62
P	BUILDING FABRIC SUNDRIES	P10	Sundry insulation/proofing work	P10	84	P10	64
		P20	Unframed isolated trims	-	-	P20	65
		P21	Ironmongery	P21	-	P21	66
		P30	Trenches/Pipeways/Pits for buried services	P30	85	P30	68
		P31	Holes/Chases for Services	P31	87	P31	69
Q	PAVING/PLANTING/ FENCING	Q23	Gravel pavings	Q23	89	Q23	70
		Q25	Slab pavings	Q25	90	Q25	70
		Q30	Turfing	Q30	91	Q30	71
		Q31	Planting	Q31	93	Q31	71
		Q40	Fencing	Q40	96	Q40	72
R	DISPOSAL SYSTEMS	R10	Rainwater pipework/gutters	R10	97	R10	74
		R11	Foul drainage above ground	R11	99	R11	75
		R12	Drainage below ground	R12	102	R12	76
S	PIPED SUPPLY SYSTEMS	S12	Hot and cold water	S12	107	S12	80
		S32	Natural gas	S32	110	S32	84
T	MECHANICAL HEATING	T32	Low temperature hot water heating	T32	111	T32	85
U	VENTILATION	U10	General extract	U10	119	U10	90
V	ELECTRICAL POWER/LIGHTING	V90	General lighting and power	V90	120	V90	91
Z	BUILDING FABRIC REFERENCE SPECIFICATIONS	Z10	Purpose made joinery	Z10	126	-	-
		Z11	Purpose made metalwork	Z11	128	-	-
		Z21	Mortars	Z21	129	-	-
GENERAL SUMMARY						GS	95

Example specification sections

F10 BRICK/BLOCK WALLING

TYPES OF WALLING

101 FACING BRICKWORK ABOVE DPC
102 FACING BRICKWORK BELOW DPC
103 FACING BLOCKWORK, 200 MM WALLS
104 FACING BLOCKWORK, 100 MM WALLS
105 COMMON BLOCKWORK BELOW DPC
106 COMMON BLOCKWORK ABOVE DPC, 200 MM WALLS
107 COMMON BLOCKWORK ABOVE DPC, 150 & 100 MM WALLS
108 ENGINEERING BRICKWORK TO MANHOLES

WORKMANSHIP GENERALLY

220 QUALITY OF WORK
230 INCLEMENT WEATHER
260 CONCRETE BRICKS/BLOCKS
290 OVERHAND LAYING
310 HEIGHT OF LIFTS
320 LEVELLING OF SEPARATE LEAVES
330 DIMENSIONS
360 BLOCKWORK
380 LINTEL BEARINGS
410 JOINTS
430 BLOCKWORK FOR PLASTER

ADDITIONAL REQUIREMENTS FOR FACEWORK

510 THE TERM FACEWORK
540 CONTROL SAMPLES
550 COLOUR MIXING
560 APPEARANCE
580 GROUND LEVEL
590 PUTLOG SCAFFOLDING
640 CLEANLINESS
650 JOINTING

A complete list of clause headings is given and, alongside, the full text of selected clauses.

101 FACING BRICKWORK ABOVE DPC:
- Bricks: Clay to BS 3921.
  Special shapes: Plinth header No 2521 D = 8 E = 159
  Plinth stretcher No 2531 D = 8 E = 41
  Manufacturer and reference: Steetley Brick Ltd: Mitford Silver Grey, smooth faced, snapped headers to curved stair wall.
- Mortar: As section Z21, Cement:lime:sand 1:1:6
- Bond: Stretching half lap.
- Joints: 5 mm square recess.

102 FACING BRICKWORK BELOW DPC:
As type F10/101 but mortar mix 1:½:3.

104 FACING BLOCKWORK, 100 MM WALLS:
- Blocks: Dense aggregate concrete to BS 6073:Part 1.
  Type: Solid.
  Work size: 390 x 190 x 140 and 90 mm
  Finish: Grit blasted on exposed faces as drawing AL(2)1.
  Special shapes (100 mm walls only): Dog leg blocks, Closer blocks to door jambs, Half blocks to curved stair walls, Lintel blocks.
  Manufacturer and reference: Edenhall Dense Masonry Blocks.
- Mortar, bond and joints as type F10/103.

540 CONTROL SAMPLES: Prepare sample panels as set out below and, after drying out, obtain approval of appearance before proceeding. Construct panels with randomly sampled bricks/blocks in an approved location.
- Walling type F10/101
  Size of panel: 1.5 m long x 1 m high
  Including example of movement joint.
- Walling type F10/104, 150 mm thick
  Size of panel: 3.0 m long x 1 m high
  Including example of course of 100 mm blocks as skirting, 135° splay and jamb (see sketch).

F30 ACCESSORIES/SUNDRY ITEMS FOR BRICK/BLOCK WALLING

FLEXIBLE DAMP PROOF COURSES/CAVITY TRAYS

030 PITCH POLYMER DAMP PROOF COURSES & CAVITY TRAYS
100 GROUND LEVEL HORIZONTAL DPCS
110 VERTICAL DPCS
120 JAMB DPCS
170 CAVITY TRAYS FORMED IN SITU
180 CAVITY TRAYS OVER OPENINGS
210 PREFORMED CAVITY TRAY JUNCTION CLOAKS
290 FACEWORK

REINFORCING/FIXING ACCESSORIES

310 CAVITY WALL TIES
315 CAVITY WALL TIES
330 FIXING CAVITY WALL TIES
350 WALL TIES
410 ANGLE SUPPORTS
420 FLAT BEARING BARS
450 JOINT REINFORCEMENT

CAVITIES

520 CLEANLINESS
540 WEEP HOLES
560 CAVITY INSULATION
570 COLD BRIDGE INSULATION
590 CAVITY CLOSERS

MOVEMENT JOINTS

650 EXPANSION JOINTS
670 SEALING OF MOVEMENT JOINTS

PROPRIETARY/MISCELLANEOUS ITEMS

760 PREFABRICATED STEEL LINTELS
880 TEMPLATES
890 WALL PLATES
950 ACOUSTICAL SEALANT POINTING
960 BLANKET SEALANT

030 PITCH POLYMER DAMP PROOF COURSES AND CAVITY TRAYS:
Manufacturer and reference:
Ruberoid Building Products Ltd: Hyload.

100 GROUND LEVEL HORIZONTAL DPCS: Lay on a thin even bed of wet mortar in a continuous strip with 100 mm laps at joints and full laps at angles. Immediately bed first course of masonry on mortar on dpc and finish joint to normal thickness.

210 PREFORMED CAVITY TRAY JUNCTION CLOAKS:
- Manufacturer: Ruberoid Building Products Ltd: Hyload.
- Type/location: External cavity cloak, purpose made for 100 mm cavity - corners of stair tower.
- Seal all laps with dpcs and/or cavity trays using adhesive/mastic/torching in accordance with manufacturer's recommendations to ensure a fully watertight installation.

310 CAVITY WALL TIES for external walls:
- To BS 1243, vertical twist type.
- Material/finish: galvanized steel.
- Sizes: 200 mm and 300 mm.
- Spacing: 600 mm horizontally, 600 mm vertically.
- Additional ties at sides of openings at 300 mm centres.

315 CAVITY WALL TIES for additional tying at window jambs where brick/block courses do not align:
- To BS 1243, vertical twist type but with no twist, twice bent.
- Material/finish: galvanized steel.
- Size: 245 mm girth.

560 CAVITY INSULATION:
- Insulation: Extruded polystyrene, size to suit wall tie spacings, thickness: 30 mm.
- Manufacturer and reference: DOW Chemicals Ltd: Styrofoam SM.
- Fixings: Vista Engineering Ltd: Vista Fix Insulation Retaining Wall Tie Clips, one to each tie.
- Ensure that edges are not damaged, top edges are covered with a temporary batten to ensure that they remain completely free of mortar droppings, grout and other debris, joints are tightly butted and all parts of the inner leaf cavity face are covered.
- Place and secure each course of insulation tight against inner leaf, before building up outer leaf above level of previous course of insulation.

T32 LOW TEMPERATURE HOT WATER HEATING

GENERALLY/DESIGN

015 SCOPE OF WORK
020 GENERAL DESCRIPTION OF THE WORK
040 INFORMATION TO BE SUBMITTED WITH TENDER
060 CO-ORDINATION
070 ELECTRICAL WORK
090 FUEL FOR TESTING

GENERAL TECHNICAL REQUIREMENTS

130 WATER TEMPERATURE AND VELOCITY
170 QUALITY OF WORK
175 BUILDER'S WORK
180 DROP RADIATORS

EQUIPMENT

210 CENTRAL HEATING BOILERS
375 BALANCED FLUE TERMINALS
470 CIRCULATING PUMPS
510 RADIATORS
515 TOWEL WARMER RADIATORS
540 RADIATOR SCHEDULE

020 GENERAL DESCRIPTION OF THE WORK:
Four house units and one tutor's flat each to have a self contained open vented LTHW system served by independent gas fired boilers with balanced flues.
Gas service to be provided by feeding off existing 100 mm gas main (specified in section S32).
Primary heating circuits: copper pipes with pumped circulation serving steel panel radiators.
Secondary heating circuits: copper pipes with pumped circulation serving towel rails in the bathrooms and shower rooms of the four house units only.
Primary hot water circuits: copper pipes with gravity circulation serving double indirect hot water combination tanks (specified in section S12), 2 no. tanks per house unit and 1 no. tank to tutor's flat.

510 RADIATORS:
- To BS 3528, Kitemark certified.
- Material: Steel
- Finish: Stoved primer
- Sizes: As clause 540
- Manufacturer: Stelrad Group Limited, PO Box 130, National Avenue, Kingston upon Hull.

540 RADIATOR SCHEDULE:

Radiator reference		Manufacturer's reference	Size H x L (mm)	Valves: M = Manual, T = Thermostatic
House Units (4 No)	R1	P2	440 x 1280	T
	R2	P2	440 x 1280	T
	R3	K2	740 x 800	M
	R4	P2	300 x 1920	T
	R5	P2	300 x 1920	T
	R6	P2	300 x 1920	T
	R7	P2	440 x 1280	T
	R8	P2	440 x 1280	T
	R9	P2	440 x 1280	T
	R10	P2	300 x 1920	T
	R11	P2	300 x 1920	T
	R12	P2	300 x 1920	T
Tutor's Flat	R1	P2	440 x 2080	T
	R2	P2	740 x 800	T
	R3	P2	300 x 3200	T
	R4	P1	440 x 1120	T
	R5	P1	440 x 1120	T
	R6	P1	740 x 480	M
	R7	P2	740 x 640	T
	R8	P2	300 x 2400	T

PIPELINES

610 COPPER PIPELINES
630 PIPE SIZES
650 PIPE RUNS
655 PIPE FIXING
660 SUPPORTS FOR COPPER PIPES
670 PIPE SPACING
675 PIPE JOINTS
690 WARNING PIPE TO FEED AND EXPANSION CISTERN
695 VENT PIPES
730 INSULATION TO PIPELINES
750 MASKING PLATES

CONTROLS

810 PROGRAMMERS
820 THERMOSTATS
840 VALVES GENERALLY
850 GATE VALVES
860 DRAIN VALVES
870 MANUAL RADIATOR VALVES
870 THERMOSTATIC RADIATOR VALVES

COMPLETION

910 TESTING AND BALANCING
930 DOCUMENTATION
940 OPERATING TOOLS
950 LABELLING

610 COPPER PIPELINES FOR HEATING SERVICES GENERALLY:
- Tube: to BS 2871:Part 1, table X, Kitemark certified.
- Jointing generally: Integral lead-free solder ring capillary fittings to BS 864:Part 2, Kitemark certified.
- Connections to equipment and fittings: Compression fittings to BS 864:Part 2, Kitemark certified.
- Supports: Concealed pipes: cast brass split munsen rings.
  Exposed pipes: strip copper machine pressings, 2 screw fixing.
  Centres as specified in clause 660.

660 SUPPORTS FOR COPPER PIPELINES: Fix securely and true to line at not more than the following centres:

Pipe diameter (mm)	Horizontal (mm)	Vertical (mm)
15	1200	1800
22 to 28	1800	2400
35 and 54	2400	3000

Provide additional supports as necessary within 150 mm of junctions and changes of direction.

870 MANUAL RADIATOR VALVES:
- Copper alloy to BS 2767.
- Finish: Matt.
- Manufacturer and reference: Hattersley: Delflo.
- Fit handwheel on flow side of radiator and lockshield on return side.

910 TESTING AND BALANCING:
- Give at least 3 days notice to SO of intention to commence testing and balancing.
- Carry out all pressure testing before fixing pipework insulation.
- Thoroughly flush out all parts of the system without contaminating circulating pump. Remove pump if necessary.
- Completely fill system, remove all air and check for leaks.
- Start boiler, run system to maximum operating temperature and check for leaks.
  Alternatively:
  Carry out hydraulic pressure test to 1½ times working pressure for a period of 30 minutes and check for leaks.
- When boiler is operating check and adjust operation of all equipment, controls and safety devices. Balance system to achieve satisfactory temperature at each heat emitter and in the domestic hot water system.
- Add an approved corrosion inhibitor.

Example quantities sections

F	MASONRY				F
	F10 BRICK/BLOCK WALLING				
	SUBSTRUCTURE				
	Facing brickwork F10/102				
	Walls				
A	Half brick thick; facework one side	24 m²			
B	Half brick thick; curved on plan 1350 mm radius; facework one side	1 m²			
	Common blockwork F10/105				
	Walls				
C	100 mm thick	98 m²			
D	100 mm thick; curved on plan 1350 mm radius	2 m²			
E	100 mm thick; curved on plan 1150 mm radius	3 m²			
F	150 mm thick	28 m²			
G	200 mm thick	105 m²			
H	200 mm thick; curved on plan 1150 mm radius	3 m²			
	SUPERSTRUCTURE				
	Facing brickwork F10/101				
	Walls				
J	Half brick thick; facework one side	253 m²			
	2/20	To collection			

F	MASONRY				F
	F10 BRICK/BLOCK WALLING (continued)				
A	Half brick thick; curved on plan 1350 mm radius; entirely of headers; facework one side	36 m²			
	Plain band				
B	75 mm wide; sunk 25 mm from face of wall; horizontal	32 m			
	Plinth capping				
C	Half brick wide; flush; horizontal; entirely of stretchers	12 m			
D	Half brick wide; flush; horizontal; entirely of headers	4 m			
	Circular opening in 300 mm cavity wall, net size of opening 1350 mm diameter lined with facing bricks on edge with radiating tapered joints, as drawing AA(2)15.				
E	Lining to half brick thick facing brickwork F10/101 ; flush; closing 50 mm cavity	5 nr			
F	Lining to 100 mm common blockwork (Spec 107); projecting 13 mm.	5 nr			
	Facing blockwork F10/103				
	Walls				
G	200 mm thick; facework one side	28 m²			
H	200 mm thick; facework both sides	119 m²			
	2/21	To collection			

	F10 BRICK/BLOCK WALLING (continued)			
	Facing blockwork F10/104			
	Walls			
A	100 mm thick; facework one side	$438\ m^2$		
B	100 mm thick; curved on plan 1150 mm radius, facework one side	$30\ m^2$		
C	100 mm thick; curved on plan 1150 mm radius; entirely of half blocks; facework one side	$36\ m^2$		
D	Extra for special 90° closer blocks	131 m		
E	Extra for special 90° dog leg blocks	120 m		
F	Extra for special 190 mm deep lintol blocks (concrete and reinforcement measured separately)	99 m		
	Common blockwork F10/106			
	Walls			
G	200 mm thick	$73\ m^2$		
	Common blockwork F10/107			
	Walls			
H	100 mm thick	$453\ m^2$		
J	150 mm thick	$37\ m^2$		
	Closing cavities			
K	50 mm wide; horizontal; blockwork 100 mm thick	26 m		
	2/22	To collection		

	F30 ACCESSORIES/SUNDRY ITEMS FOR BRICK/BLOCK WALLING			
	SUBSTRUCTURE			
	Forming cavities in hollow walls			
A	50 mm wide; wall ties F30/310	$8\ m^2$		
B	100 mm wide; wall ties F30/310	$117\ m^2$		
	SUPERSTRUCTURE			
	Forming cavities in hollow walls			
C	50 mm wide; wall ties F30/310; cavity insulation F30/560, 30 mm thick	$15\ m^2$		
D	Extra for additional special ties F30/315, 345 mm long at sides of openings	92 nr		
E	100 mm wide; wall ties Spec 310; cavity insulation Spec 560, 300 mm thick	$213\ m^2$		
F	100 mm wide; wall ties Spec 310; cavity insulation Spec 560, 30 mm thick, curved on plan 1300 mm radius	$33\ m^2$		
	Damp proof courses F30/030-290			
	On surfaces			
G	Not exceeding 225 mm wide; horizontal	$69\ m^2$		
H	Not exceeding 225 mm wide; horizontal; curved on plan	$2\ m^2$		
J	Not exceeding 225 mm wide; vertical	$5\ m^2$		
K	110 mm wide; vertical; to circular window opening, 1330 mm net diameter.	5 nr		
	Cavity trays			
L	Exceeding 225 mm wide; horizontal	$3\ m^2$		
	2/23	To collection		

	T32 LOW TEMPERATURE HOT WATER HEATING			
	Copper pipelines T32/610			
	Pipework			
A	15 mm diameter	24 m		
B	15 mm diameter; to concrete or masonry	249 m		
C	Extra for fittings, two ends	98 nr		
D	Extra for fittings, three ends	10 nr		
E	22 mm diameter; to concrete or masonry	131 m		
F	Extra for fittings, two ends	48 nr		
G	Extra for fittings, three ends	24 nr		
H	28 mm diameter	99 m		
J	28 mm diameter; to concrete or masonry	50 m		
K	Extra for fittings, two ends	75 nr		
L	Extra for fittings, three ends	36 nr		
M	35 mm diameter	47 m		
N	35 mm diameter; to concrete or masonry	59 m		
P	Extra for fittings, two ends	50 nr		
Q	Extra for fittings, three ends	22 nr		
R	Extra for flanged connection to equipment	20 nr		
	Gate valves T32/850			
S	28 mm diameter; joints to copper pipes	20 nr		
T	35 mm diameter; joints to copper pipes	28 nr		
	Drain valves T32/860			
U	15 mm diameter; joints to copper pipes	20 nr		

(Pages 2/86, 2/87 and 2/88 not shown)

	T32 LOW TEMPERATURE HOT WATER HEATING (continued)			
	Type P2; brackets to concrete or masonry			
A	300 x 1920 mm	24 nr		
B	300 x 2400 mm	1 nr		
C	300 x 3200 mm	1 nr		
D	440 x 1280 mm	20 nr		
E	440 x 2080 mm	1 nr		
F	740 x 640 mm	1 nr		
G	740 x 800 mm	5 nr		
	Insulation T32/730			
	Pipelines			
H	28 mm diameter	99 m		
J	35 mm diameter	47 m		
	Testing, balancing and commissioning T32/910			
	System generally			
K	Preparatory operations	item		
L	Pressure testing	item		
M	Balancing	item		
		To collection		
	COLLECTION Page 2/85			
	" 2/86			
	" 2/87			
	" 2/88			
	" 2/89			

Example 1
Collections located at end of each group of sections.

GENERAL SUMMARY

		Page
A	Preliminaries/General conditions (Including Dayworks, PC and Provisional Sums)	A 9
D	Groundwork	D 11
E	In situ/Large precast concrete	E 19
F	Masonry	F 26
G	Structural/Carcassing metal/timber	G 32
H	Cladding/Covering	H 40
J	Waterproofing	J 41
K	Linings	K 44
L	Windows/Door/Stairs	L 51
M	Surface finishes	M 60
N	Furniture/Equipment	N 63
P	Building fabric sundries	P 69
Q	Paving/Planting/Fencing	Q 73
R	Disposal systems	R 79
S	Piped supply systems	S 84
T	Mechanical heating	T 89
U	Ventilation	U 90
V	Electrical power/lighting	V 94

PAGE 2/95 TOTAL CARRIED TO FORM OF TENDER

Example 2
Collections located at end of each work section. Each section has its own total, but the bill is longer and the General Summary runs to two pages.

GENERAL SUMMARY

		Page	
A1	The project generally	A1	1
A2	The Contract	A2	2
A3	Employer's requirements	A3	3
A4	Contractor's general cost items	A4	5
A5	Work by others or subject to instruction (Including Dayworks, PC and Provision Sums)	A5	9
D20	Excavating and filling	D20	11
E10	In situ concrete	E10	14
E20	Formwork for in situ concrete	E20	16
E30	Reinforcement for in situ concrete	E30	17
E40	Designed joints in in situ concrete	E40	18
E41	Worked finishes to in situ concrete	E41	19
E60	Precast concrete decking	E60	20
F10	Brick/Block walling	F10	23
F30	Accessories/Sundry items for brick/block walling	F30	26
G10	Structural steel framing	G10	27
G20	Carpentry/First fixing	G10	33
H10	Patent glazing	H10	35
H31	Metal profiled sheet covering	H31	37
H71	Lead sheet flashings	H71	39
H74	Zinc sheet coverings/flashings	H74	42
J40	Flexible sheet damp proof membranes	J40	43
K10	Plasterboard dry lining	K10	44
K11	Rigid sheet flooring/sheathing		
L10	Timber windows	[illegible]	79
L11	Metal windo[illegible]	R10	80
L1[illegible]	[illegible] ground	R11	82
	[illegible]age below ground	R12	86
S12	Hot and cold water	S12	90
S32	Natural gas	S32	91
T32	Low temperature hot water heating	T32	96
U10	General extract	U10	97
V90	General lighting and power	V90	101

PAGE 2/103 TOTAL CARRIED TO FORM OF TENDER

Implications for contractors

Generally

For contractors, CPI should mean pricing and building with greater confidence and less risk. CPI should ensure that drawings, specifications and quantities are more thorough and complete, giving contractors greater scope to exercise their organisational and commercial skills. It should mean that more time can be spent on managing and controlling the work, less on chasing information, coping with disruptions and preparing claims.

But 'thorough' and 'complete' are relative terms, and clearly the quality of CPI will vary from design team to design team and job to job. Therefore contractors will be well advised to check the state of the drawings in some detail (if necessary by visiting the designers' offices) and assess the reliability of the specification before tendering. Good quality CPI can make all the difference between a good job and a bad one, and a thorough examination of the documents at the outset will be time well spent.

Tendering

Co-ordinated project information and SMM7 are being introduced at the same time, and clearly have a strong association. SMM7 based quantities will be simpler than those based on previous editions and estimators will have to adjust the basis of their pricing to allow for the new rules.

CPI means that the design team must take greater care in preparing documents for main contractors to price; main contractors, in their turn, should take care when preparing documentation for issue to sub-contractors. The provision to tendering sub-contractors of nothing more than a few pages of measured items will now be even more unacceptable.

It is fundamental to the CPI concept that both tendering contractors and sub-contractors be provided with:

- Measured quantities (with quantities contracts only).
- Full specification information.
- Adequate drawings.
- Relevant preliminaries requirements.

The process of dividing up and editing the quantities and specification for sub-contract tendering should be simplified by the 'small scope' work sections of the Common Arrangement. For example, the student residences project included 15 sub-contracts, with a total value of 43% of the Contract Sum. Figure S on page 58 shows how they were made up – in only two cases was it necessary to split a work section.

Programming

To be of maximum value, programmes should be prepared early. CPI should help to ensure that the information needed by the contractor for preparation of his programme is available.

It is clearly advantageous for building programmes to be capable of being read in conjunction with the project drawings, specification and quantities. Figure R shows the contractor's programme for the example student residences project re-stated in terms of CAWS and reflecting the division of work between different sub-contractors and work-gangs. Cross-references to the relevant CAWS sections are given so that each activity on the programme can be traced back to the relevant specification requirements, quantities and monetary values. In this way the programme can form an effective extension of the co-ordinated project information, facilitating management in respect of both time and cost.

Quality control

If the project information as a whole is well co-ordinated, comprehensive and provided in good time, the contractor's site agent (and clerk of works) will need to spend much less time than is presently the norm in 'filling the gaps'. This should mean that they have more time available for organising the work and controlling progress and quality on a day to day basis. The result should be that work is executed more efficiently and to more consistent standards of quality.

The availability of a comprehensive project specification should ensure that the site agent and clerk of works are able to work to definitive standards of quality. The specification should set out clear requirements for samples, testing, inspections and approvals at defined stages in the work.

In conclusion

Co-ordinated project information offers benefits to everyone involved in the design/build process, not least contractors. Greater efficiency, better control of time, quality and cost and more harmonious working relations are likely to stem from the national CPI initiative. The ultimate beneficiaries will be the industry's clients.

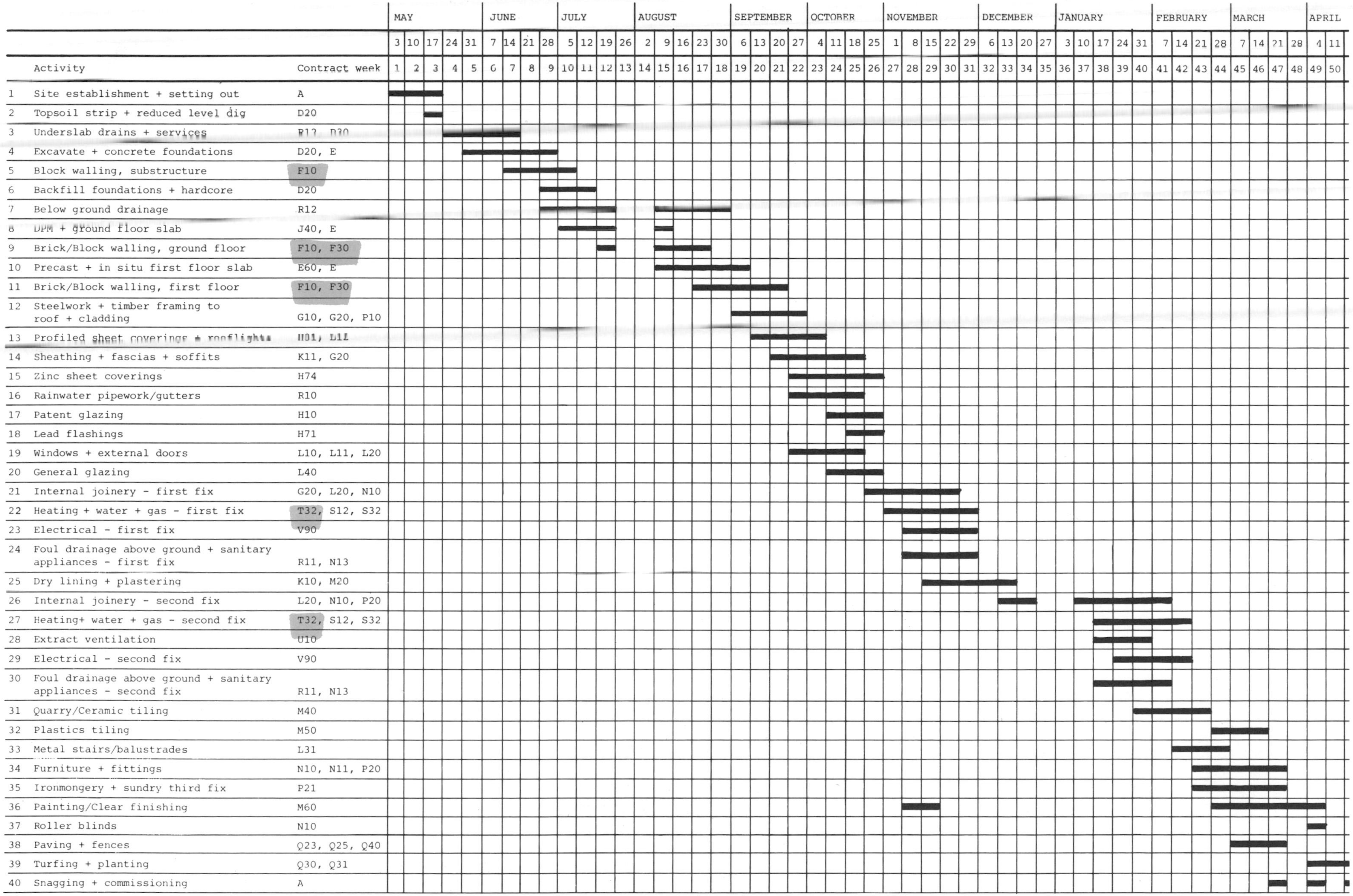

	MAY					JUNE				JULY				AUGUST					SEPTEMBER				OCTOBER				NOVEMBER					DECEMBER				JANUARY					FEBRUARY				MARCH				APRIL	
	3	10	17	24	31	7	14	21	28	5	12	19	26	2	9	16	23	30	6	13	20	27	4	11	18	25	1	8	15	22	29	6	13	20	27	3	10	17	24	31	7	14	21	28	7	14	21	28	4	11
Contract week	1	2	3	4	5	6	7	8	9	10	11	12	13	14	15	16	17	18	19	20	21	22	23	24	25	26	27	28	29	30	31	32	33	34	35	36	37	38	39	40	41	42	43	44	45	46	47	48	49	50

	Activity	Contract week
1	Site establishment + setting out	A
2	Topsoil strip + reduced level dig	D20
3	Underslab drains + services	R12, D30
4	Excavate + concrete foundations	D20, E
5	Block walling, substructure	F10
6	Backfill foundations + hardcore	D20
7	Below ground drainage	R12
8	DPM + ground floor slab	J40, E
9	Brick/Block walling, ground floor	F10, F30
10	Precast + in situ first floor slab	E60, E
11	Brick/Block walling, first floor	F10, F30
12	Steelwork + timber framing to roof + cladding	G10, G20, P10
13	Profiled sheet coverings + rooflights	H31, L12
14	Sheathing + fascias + soffits	K11, G20
15	Zinc sheet coverings	H74
16	Rainwater pipework/gutters	R10
17	Patent glazing	H10
18	Lead flashings	H71
19	Windows + external doors	L10, L11, L20
20	General glazing	L40
21	Internal joinery - first fix	G20, L20, N10
22	Heating + water + gas - first fix	T32, S12, S32
23	Electrical - first fix	V90
24	Foul drainage above ground + sanitary appliances - first fix	R11, N13
25	Dry lining + plastering	K10, M20
26	Internal joinery - second fix	L20, N10, P20
27	Heating+ water + gas - second fix	T32, S12, S32
28	Extract ventilation	U10
29	Electrical - second fix	V90
30	Foul drainage above ground + sanitary appliances - second fix	R11, N13
31	Quarry/Ceramic tiling	M40
32	Plastics tiling	M50
33	Metal stairs/balustrades	L31
34	Furniture + fittings	N10, N11, P20
35	Ironmongery + sundry third fix	P21
36	Painting/Clear finishing	M60
37	Roller blinds	N10
38	Paving + fences	Q23, Q25, Q40
39	Turfing + planting	Q30, Q31
40	Snagging + commissioning	A

Figure R Works programme for student residences

		Work sections	Programme activities
1.	Topsoil strip + reduced level dig	D20 (part)	2
2.	Patent glazing	H10	17
3.	Profiled sheet coverings	H31	13
	Plastics rooflights	L12	13
4.	Lead flashings	H71	18
	Rainwater pipework/gutters	R10	16
	Foul drainage above ground	R11	24 + 30
	Sanitary appliances	N13	24 + 30
5.	Zinc sheet coverings	H74	15
6.	Plasterboard dry lining	K10	25
	Plastered/Rendered coatings	M20	25
7.	Metal stairs/balustrades	L31	33
8.	General glazing	L40	20
9.	Quarry/Ceramic tiling	M40	31
10.	Plastics tiling	M50	32
11.	Painting/Clear finishing	M60	36
12.	Roller blinds	N10 (part)	37
13.	Turfing	Q30	39
	Planting	Q31	39
14.	Hot and cold water	S12	22 + 27
	Natural gas	S32	22 + 27
	Low temperature hot water heating	T32	22 + 27
	Extract ventilation	U10	28
15.	Electrical power/lighting	V90	23 + 29

Figure S Sub-contracts for student residences

Appendix 1 Large projects: the relationship between quality of information, site management and quality of finished work.

Key: Poor (dark shading) / Average (light shading) / Good (no shading)

Type of building (Traditional contract if not stated otherwise)	Completeness & promptness of drawings & specification	Information support provided by designers on site	Quality of Clerk of Works	Quality of Contractor's management	General quality of completed work	Special features
Training Camp	Poor	Poor	Average	Average	Poor	Contractor demoralised by very poor information. C of W, with no support from Architect, was powerless.
Offices (Management contract)	Poor	Average	None	Poor	Poor	Drawings late. Large but inexperienced Contractor's site management team could not control poor sub-contractors.
Barracks (Design and build)	Poor	Average	Average	Average	Poor	Late and incomplete drawings, despite form of contract. C of W had no 'teeth' because of form of contract. Poor day to day control by Contractor.
Training Centre (Construction management)	Poor	Average	Average	Average	Average	Very late and incomplete services information. Contractor's day to day control was poor.
Records Office	Poor	Average	Good	Average	Average	Drawings insufficiently detailed. Contractor's management team too small. Excellent C of W's team got reasonable results despite difficulties.
Offices (Design and build)	Poor	Average	None	Good	Average	Drawings late, despite form of contract. Initially a 'problem' project, but new Contractor's management team effectively retrieving the situation.
Offices and Shops (Management contract)	Poor	Average	Average	Good	Good	Drawings late and unco-ordinated. Good selection of sub-contractors and good overall management offset poor information.
Crown Court	Poor	Good	Average	Good	Good	Drawings late and not always complete, but offset by on site team of drawings co-ordinators. Large and effective Contractor's management team.
Offices	Poor	Good	None	Good	Good	Full time Site Architect filled in missing information. Excellent teamwork on site.
Barracks refurbishment	Average	Average	Good	Average	Good	Mainly demolition work at time of survey. Capable C of W.
Offices refurbishment	Average	Average	Good	Good	Good	Drawings did not take account of inaccuracy of existing structure. Extremely capable C of W and competent Contractor's management team overcame deficiencies in drawings.
Offices (Design and build)	Average	Average	Average	Good	Good	Architects failed to commit sufficient resources to project. Excellent site team overcame poor information.
Offices (Management contract)	Good	Average	None	Poor	Poor	Good information. Poor selection of sub-contractors, and ineffective Contractor's site management led to very poor work.
Airport Terminal (Construction management)	Good	Good	Average	Good	Good	Reasonably timely and complete drawings. Extremely proficient Contractor's site team.
Department Store (Management contract)	Good	Good	None	Good	Good	Good information. Contractor selected tried and trusted sub-contractors. Experienced Contractor's site team.
Offices	Good	Good	Good	Good	Good	Excellent drawings and full specification. Efficient, well co-ordinated construction team ensured good quality in tight contract time.

Appendix 2 Medium size projects: the relationship between quality of information, site management and quality of finished work.

Key: Poor / Average / Good

Type of building (Traditional contract if not stated otherwise)	Completeness & promptness of drawings & specification	Information support provided by designers on site	Quality of Clerk of Works	Quality of Contractor's management	General quality of completed work	Special features
Warehouse & Offices	Poor	Average	Average	Poor	Poor	Drawings late and incomplete. C of W had no authority. Inexperienced Site Agent failed to co-ordinate and control sub-contractors.
Offices	Poor	Average	Poor	Poor	Poor	Drawings late and not very explicit. Incompetent Site Agent. Visiting C of W rarely visited the site. No-one interested in the job.
Equipment Centres (Several sites)	Poor	Average	Poor	Good	Average	Drawings incomplete and insufficiently detailed. Conscientious Site Agent and tradesmen became demoralised by poor information. Visiting C of W had no authority.
Offices	Poor	Average	Poor	Good	Average	Drawings late and insufficiently detailed. Good Contractor's site team could not quite overcome problem of poor information. Visiting junior C of W.
Shops and Offices	Poor	Average	None	Good	Good	Drawings late and incomplete. Confident, competent and committed Site Agent produced good work despite poor information.
Offices (Design and build)	Poor	Average	None	Good	Good	Drawings very incomplete. Experienced Site Agent overcame deficiencies in information to satisfy inquisitive Client.
Laboratories & Offices	Poor	Average	Average	Average	Average	Services drawings late, impractical and not co-ordinated with Architect's drawings. No site supervision by Services Designer or Services Contractor. Site agent and C of W worn down by this – the whole building suffered.
Equipment Centre	Poor	Good	Poor	Good	Good	Drawings unco-ordinated and lacking in detail. Excellent Site Agent developed good liaison with Architect's Technician. C of W ineffective.
Offices	Average	Poor	Average	Average	Average	Drawings adequate. C of W had poor back up from Architect. Site Agent of average ability, but no-one really in control.
Housing	Average	Average	Poor	Poor	Poor	Drawings adequate. Low calibre sub-contractors skimping work. Contractor's site management virtually non-existent. Visiting C of W ineffective.
Equipment Centre	Average	Average	Good	Good	Good	Drawings adequate. Competent Site Agent and C of W worked well together to produce an excellent job.
Offices and Workshops (Traditional, negotiated)	Average	Good	None	Good	Good	Drawings reasonably complete and timely, well backed up verbally by Architect. Competent Site Agent planned and controlled the job firmly and well.
Factory extension	Good	Good	Good	Poor	Good	Drawings timely and complete. Full specification. Architect and C of W achieved reasonably successful outcome despite inexperienced and ineffective Site Agent.
Office refurbishment (Management contract)	Good	Average	None	Good	Good	Drawings timely and complete. Experienced and well trained Contractor's site management team.

Appendix 3 Small projects: the relationship between quality of information, site management and quality of finished work.

Key: Poor (dark shading) · Average (light shading) · Good (no shading)

Type of building (Traditional contract if not stated otherwise)	Completeness & promptness of drawings & specification	Information support provided by designers on site	Quality of Clerk of Works	Quality of Contractor's management	General quality of completed work	Special features
Equipment Centre	Poor	Poor	Good	Poor	Poor	Many mistakes on drawings. Low grade and ineffective Site Agent. Extremely capable C of W could not overcome the difficulties.
Cottage Hospital	Poor	Average	Good	Poor	Average	Drawn details lacking or poorly worked out. Site Agent failed to control the job. C of W restricted his involvement to inspection, so did not compensate for deficiencies of others.
School refurbishment and extension	Poor	Average	Good	Average	Average	Drawings poorly co-ordinated and incomplete. Site Agent reluctant to exercise any control. Quality saved by conscientious workmen.
Hotel extension	Average	Average	Good	Good	Good	Only a few information problems. Good Site Agent. Site observed at early stage only; quality good.
Training centre	Average	Average	Good	Poor	Good	Drawings adequate. Site Agent lacked commitment and failed to control the job. Extremely competent C of W with good back up from Client was able to get results.
Several small buildings	Average	Good	Good	Average	Good	Drawings adequate; Architect often on site to answer queries. Little forward planning but good day to day control. Very authoritative C of W.
School (Design and manage by Architect)	Good	Good	Average	Good	Good	Drawings timely and complete; Architect often on site. Informal but effective control by Architect and Site Agent.
Hostel Extension	Good	Good	Good	Good	Good	Drawings timely and complete; Architect often on site. Informal but effective control by Architect, C of W and Site Agent.

Where the CPI documents may be obtained

Document	Source	Telephone
Common arrangement of work sections Production Drawings Code Project Specification Code	Association of Consulting Engineers, Alliance House, 12 Caxton Street, London SW1H 0QL	01 222 6557
	BEC Publications, 2309 Coventry Road, Sheldon, Birmingham B26 3PL (Mail order only)	021 742 0824
	Building Centre Bookshop, 26 Store Street, London WC1E 7BT	01 637 1022
	RIBA Publications, 66 Portland Place, London W1N 4AD (Personal shoppers only)	01 580 5533
	RIBA Publications, Finsbury Mission, Moreland Street, London EC1V 8VB (Mail order only)	01 251 0791
	Surveyor's Bookshop, 12 Great George Street, London SW1P 3AD (Personal shoppers only)	01 222 7000
	Surveyor's Publications, Norden House, Basing View, Basingstoke, Hants RG21 2HN (Mail order only)	0256 55234
SMM Seventh Edition Bills of Quantities code	BEC Publications Building Centre Bookshop RIBA Publications Surveyor's Bookshop Surveyor's Publications	See above
National Building Specification	NBS Services, Mansion House Chambers, The Close, Newcastle upon Tyne NE1 3RE	091 232 9594
National Engineering Specification	NES Ltd, Southgate Chambers, 37–39 Southgate Street, Winchester S023 9EH	0962 842 058
SMM7 Standard Descriptions	BEC Publications Surveyor's Bookshop Surveyor's Publications	See above

Full titles of the documents are given on the inside of the front cover. Prices on application.